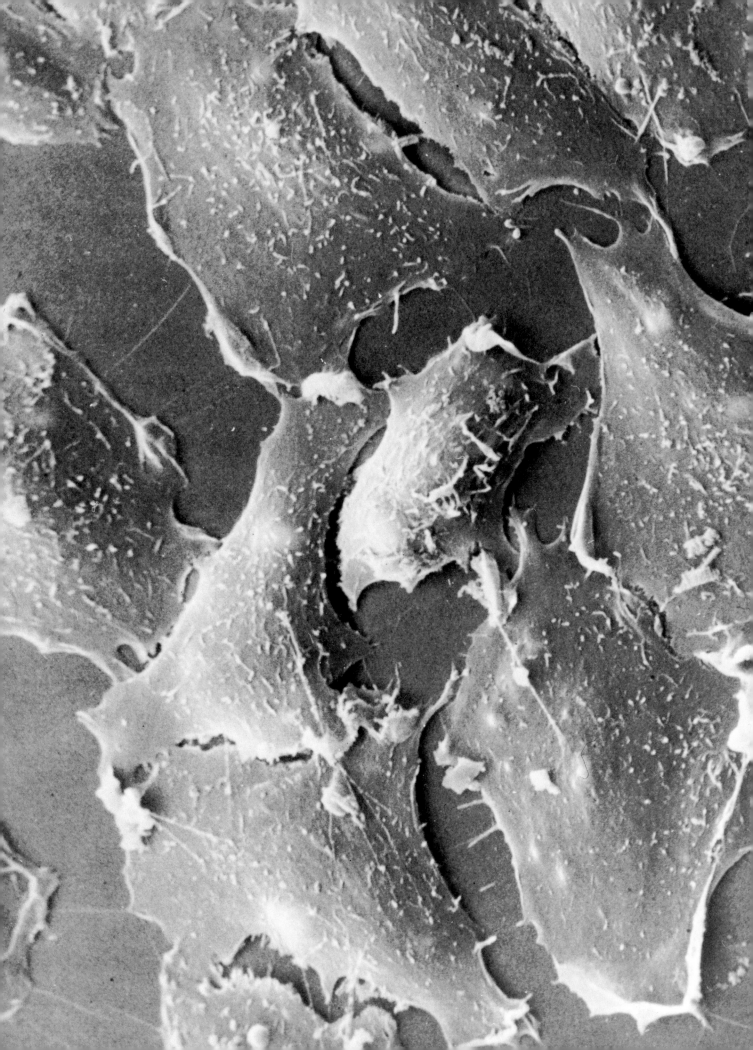

Scanning Electronmicrograph of Chinese Hamster
Cells Growing in Tissue Culture

*These cells are growing essentially independently.
While they are probably influenced somewhat by
the presence of each other, they have not become
organized into a tissue.*

*It seems an appropriate frontispiece for a disser-
tation on cell structure:*

*First, because it shows cells in their entirety and
from the outside;*

*Second, because it is desirable to have a concept
of a thing as a whole before concentrating on
the minutia of its component parts;*

*Third, because the micrograph represents one of
the newer techniques for examining cells which
makes possible the direct observation of aspects
of their structure that hitherto had to be inferred;*

*Lastly, because it is easily seen that scattered
over the surface of these cells are many small
projections (microvilli), structures which are
peculiarly characteristic of cells like these that
have undergone malignant change, and this is one
of many observations on such renegade cells that
is still unexplained and thus indicative of the
necessarily unfinished nature of whatever we
may write today about cells.*

Scope® Monograph on

CYTOLOGY

The Cell and Its Nucleus

A. G. Macleod M.D.

formerly of the Faculty, University of Michigan
School of Medicine and Rockefeller University,
presently consultant to The Upjohn Company

Published by The Upjohn Company, Kalamazoo, Michigan

Baird A. Thomas,
Editor

Preface

The idea of writing a short treatise on cytology started with the preparation of a booklet to accompany a large (24' in diameter) model of a cell which was shown at the 1958 annual meeting of The American Medical Association in San Francisco and later was for a number of years at the Museum of Science & Industry in Chicago. Since the booklet was not only intended to explain the exhibit but also to document the way in which the cell organelles were portrayed, extensive use was made of original electron micrographs. Consequently, many medical students and others who had never seen the exhibit found the book useful.

While the Cell exhibit has served its purpose and has been dismantled, the booklet has outlived its original function and seems to have found a *raison d'etre* of its own. Subsequently, another exhibit with an accompanying booklet dealing with the nucleus and entitled *Genes in Action* was prepared and again the booklet has found a usefulness apart from the exhibit which is now on display in the Cleveland Health Museum. It seems logical to update and combine these booklets, particularly since a number of eminent scientists generously gave us a great deal of assistance and all this effort should not be wasted.

In this updating process we have again received generous cooperation from many of the scientists who are persistently enlarging this field of knowledge. Curiously they are also breaking down the borderlines between the various disciplines of Biology. As a result the biochemistry of an organelle has become an important criterion for its recognition and electron micrographs are of frequent occurrence in the writings of biochemists. Hence, the new terms 'Cell Biology' and 'Molecular Biology' are being used more and more. Indeed, the old division of Biology into such disciplines as Morphology, Biochemistry, Physiology, etc., was based more on the tools that the investigator was skilled in using than the problem.

Today more attention is paid to the problem and the investigators seize on whatever tools will serve. As a corollary, a group of investigators attacking a problem are likely to have diverse and assorted skills. The human animal has not transcended his limitations; we do not have supermen but well-organized teams.

In writing this book my purpose has been only to introduce the reader to the subject so that he can more easily pursue his studies further. To this end a short bibliography is included.

The present volume has been possible only because of the generous assistance of the busy investigators who have taken the many fine electron micrographs, which we are privileged to reproduce. The list, on the following pages, of those to whom we (the reader and I) are indebted is an impressive one.

Acknowledgements

Wolfgang Beerman. Max Plank Institut fur Biologie, Tubingen, Germany. Fig. 82

Gary Bennett and C. P. LeBlond. Department of Anatomy, McGill University, Montreal, Canada. Figs. 38, 39, 40, 41

R. M. Brown, Jr. University of North Carolina, Chapel Hill, North Carolina. Fig. 42

Ulrich Clever. Department of Biology, Purdue University, Lafayette, Indiana. Figs. 79, 80, 83, 97

H. Colomb and G. F. Bahr. Armed Forces Institute of Pathology, Bethesda, Maryland. Figs. 100a and b

John W. Combs. Milton S. Hershey Medical Center, Pennsylvania State University, Hershey, Pennsylvania. Fig. 43

Ellen R. Dirksen. University of California, School of Medicine, San Francisco, California. Figs. 12, 55

William O. Dobbins III, M.D. Veterans Administration Hospital, Washington, D.C. Fig. 4

Don W. Fawcett, M.D. Department of Anatomy, Harvard Medical School, Boston, Massachusetts. Figs. 2, 5, 16, 27, 50a and b, 63

W. H. Finley, Ph.D., M.D. and S. C. Finley, M.D. School of Medicine, University of Alabama, Birmingham, Alabama. Figs. 72, 73, 74

Daniel S. Friend. University of California School of Medicine, San Francisco, California. Figs. 19, 30, 35, 36, 37

Joseph C. Gall. Yale University, New Haven, Connecticut. Figs. 76, 77, 95

Leonard D. Hamilton. Brookhaven National Laboratory, Upton, Long Island, New York. Figs. 86, 87

Douglas E. Kelly, M.D. University of Washington School of Medicine, Seattle, Washington. Fig. 48

W. J. Larsen. Case Western Reserve University, Cleveland, Ohio. Fig. 26

John H. Luft, Department of Biological Structure, University of Washington, School of Medicine, Seattle, WA

C. F. McCall, I. Katayma, R. S. Cotran and M. Finland. Thorndike Memorial Laboratory, Second and Fourth (Harvard) Medical Services and Mallory Institute of Pathology, Boston County Hospital and the Department of Medicine and Pathology, Harvard Medical School. Fig. 44

J. Richard McIntosh, University of Colorado, Boulder, Colorado. Fig. 65

O. L. Miller, Jr. Oak Ridge National Laboratory, Biological Division, Oak Ridge, Tennessee. Figs. 78, 93, 94

O. L. Miller, Jr. and Barbara Ann Hambrate. Oak Ridge National Laboratory, Biological Division, Oak Ridge, Tennessee. Fig. 108

O. L. Miller, Jr. and Barbara R. Beatty. Oak Ridge National Laboratory, Biological Division, Oak Ridge, Tennessee. Figs. 101, 102, 103

George D. Pappas. New York University School of Medicine, New York, New York. Fig. 34

Keith R. Porter. University of Colorado, Boulder, Colorado. Frontispiece, 1, 9, 11, 13, 14, 15, 20, 29, 31, 33, 47, 49, 51, 52, 53, 56

E. L. Powers, C. F. Ehret, L. E. Roth, O. T. Melnick. Argonne National Laboratory, Argonne, Illinois. Fig. 18

H. C. Renger, Ph.D. Department of Pathology, New York University Medical Center, New York, New York. Figs. 23, 24a

J. P. Revel. Department of Anatomy, Harvard Medical School, Boston, Massachusetts. Fig. 6

J. P. Revel and D. A. Goodenough. Harvard Medical School, Boston, Massachusetts. Fig. 7

Hans Ris and Barbara Chandler. Department of Zoology, University of Wisconsin, Madison, Wisconsin. Figs. 92, 99, 106

Russell Ross and Earl P. Benditt. Department of Pathology, University of Washington, Seattle, Washington. Fig. 107

Dr. Sasamu Ito. Department of Anatomy, Harvard Medical School, Boston, Massachusetts. Fig. 10

A. W. Sedar, Ph.D. Jefferson Medical College, Philadelphia, Pennsylvania. Fig. 17

Margery Shaw. Department of Biology, M. D. Anderson Hospital, Houston, Texas. Figs. 66, 69, 75

A. H. Sparrow. Brookhaven National Laboratory, Upton, Long Island, New York. Fig. 67

Hewson Swift and Barbara Jean Stevens. Whitman Laboratory, University of Chicago, Chicago, Illinois. Figs. 81, 89, 96, 98a

Theodore N. Tahmisian, R. L. Devine. Argonne National Laboratory, Argonne, Illinois. Fig. 25

Lewis G. Tilney. University of Pennsylvania, Philadelphia, Pennsylvania. Figs. 54, 57, 58, 59, 60, 61, 62

Davis R. Wolstenholm. University of Utah, Salt Lake City, Utah. Figs. 23, 24, 98b and c

Dorothea Zucker-Franklin. Department of Medicine, New York University Medical Center, New York, New York. Figs. 45, 46

In addition to the scientists, we are indebted to the following journals for permission to reproduce illustrations that have appeared in their pages.

Federation Proceedings
Journal of Cell Biology
Journal of Cell Physiology
Journal of Experimental Medicine
Journal of Ultrastructural Research
Proceedings of the National Academy of Science
Science

The portraits of Antonti van Leeuwenhoek, Jean de Lamark, Mathias Schleiden and Theodor Schwann were obtained from Bettmann Archive Inc., New York, N.Y.

A Tribute

The eminent designer, Mr. Will Burtin, to whom we owe the elegant appearance of both original exhibits and the booklets that accompanied them, died on January 18, 1972. He found much that was beautiful in science and was able by his dramatic presentation of these truths to infect others with his enthusiasm. The elegance with which he clothed the scientific concepts he was given to present acted as a sort of active transport system across the science-brain barrier.

He not only furthered the comprehension of science by making it palatable, he made scientific demonstrations into notable works of art. Art and science have lost a devoted liaison officer.

Editor's Note

It is with great sorrow that we report that Dr. A. G. Macleod died suddenly and unexpectedly on December 27, 1972. It will be difficult indeed for Dr. Macleod's many friends, as it is for us, to realize that his vast knowledge, infinite patience and brilliant but demanding use of easily readable sentence structure are at an end.

It is fortunate for us, as well as his future audiences, that the final details relative to this monograph production had been checked and rechecked prior to his death.

As with the passing of all talented people, the world will never know what other masterpiece might have emanated from the pen of this gifted man. However, we feel assured that this last effort will be widely acclaimed as a fitting finale to his great ability.

1665 • *Robert Hooke*

1674 • *Antoni van Leeuwenhoek*

Development of the cell concept

1656 • *Pierre Borel reported microscopic studies of many objects, among them what were probably human red blood cells.*

1661 • *Marcello Malpighi, who discovered capillaries, may have referred to cells when he spoke of "utricles," "globules," and "saccules."*

1665 • *Robert Hooke published his* Micrographia, *wherein he described his examination of a piece of cork. This was not only the first application of the word "cell" to the biologic entity that the word now designates but may have been the first use of a thin section to reveal microscopic structures.*

1672 • *Nehemiah Grew published the first of two well-illustrated volumes on the microscopic anatomy of plants; he described minute "utricles" or "vesicles."*

1674 • *Antoni van Leeuwenhoek, who improved the art of polishing short-focal-length lenses, reported his discovery of protozoa in a letter to the Royal Society of London; in other letters published over a period of more than fifty years he reported discovery of bacteria, rotifers, and other microscopic organisms.*

1759 • *Kaspar Friedrich Wolff, founder of embryology, noted in* Theoria Generationis *that "the particles which constitute all animal organs in their earliest inception are little globules, which may be distinguished under a microscope."*

1802 • *Charles Francois Brisseau de Mirbel observed in his* Traite d'anatomie et de physiologie Vegetales *that "Plants appear to be entirely composed of cells and of tubes, all parts of which are continuous."*

1805 • *Lorenz Oken hypothesized in* Die Zeugung *that "Animals and plants are throughout nothing else than manifoldly divided or repeated vesicles."*

1831 • *Robert Brown*

1809 • *Jean de Lamarck*

1809 • *Jean Baptiste Pierre Antoine de Monet de Lamarck,* in Philosophie Zoologique, *stated that "No body can possess life if its containing parts are not of cellular tissue or formed by cellular tissue."*

1824 • *R. J. H. Dutrochet wrote in* Recherches anatomique et physiologiques *"All organic tissues are actually globular cells of exceeding smallness, which appear to be united only by simple adhesive forces."*

1826 • *J. P. F. Turpin, in his memoir* Organographie Microscopique elementaire et comparée des vegetaux, *summarized his findings in his title: "Observations on the origin and first formation of cellular tissue, on the vesicles composing this tissue, considered as distinct individualities having their own vital center of vegetation and propagation and destined to form by agglomeration the composite individuality of all those plants whose organization is composed of more than one vesicle."*

1830 • *F. J. F. Meyen wrote, in his* Phytotomie, *"Plant cells appear either singly . . . or they are united together . . . to constitute a more highly organized plant. Even in this case each cell forms an independent isolated whole; it nourishes itself, builds itself up, and elaborates raw nutrient materials . . . into very different substances."*

1831 • *Robert Brown reported to the Linnean Society his discovery of the cell nucleus. He used a simple or single lense microscope.*

1832 • *B. C. Dumortier, in* Recherches sur la structure comparée developpement des animaux et des vegetaux, *reported cell division in algae.*

1835-39 • *Hugo von Mohl described many details of cell division.*

1838 • *Mathias Jakob Schleiden published his* Beiträge zur Phytogenese, *explaining the derivation of plant tissues from cells.*

1838 • *Mathias Jakob Schleiden*

1839 • *Theodor Schwann*

1866 • *Gregor Mendel*

1858 • *Rudolf Virchow*

1869 • *Friedrich Miescher*

1875 • *Eduard Strasburger*

1876 • *Walther Flemming*

1839 • *Theodor Schwann published his* Mikroskopische Untersuchungen über die Uebereinstimmung in der Struktur und dem Wachsthum der Thiere und Pflanzen, *in which he applied Schleiden's cell theory to animal tissues and emphasized that "cells are organisms and entire animals and plants are aggregates of these organisms arranged according to definite laws."*
The treatises of Schleiden & Schwann established the "cell theory" as an important biological concept.

1842 • *Karl Nägeli, while observing the division of plant cells, saw and described chromosomes; but he did not appreciate their significance and was not able to demonstrate that the process he observed was not just a peculiarity of the species he was studying.*
Thus it is seen that cell morphology was already a well-established science before 1850.

1858 • *Rudolf Virchow with the publication of his "Cellular Pathology" applied the cell theory to pathology, expressing his belief that pathologic changes had their origin in the cell. He also, in 1858, put forth his theory of cell lineage which pointed out "if present cells have come from pre-existing cells, then all cells can trace their ancestry back to the first formed cell in an unbroken line of descent." This idea clearly related cytology to embryology, heredity and evolution.*

1866 • *Gregor Mendel published the results of his experiments on the inheritance of pea plants. With this the science of genetics can be said to have had its origin. Mendel's analysis of his results was both original and ingenious; he was obviously aware of discrete units of heredity such as we now call genes. He laid a firm foundation for the new science even though it was almost half a century before the importance of his experimental results was realized.*

1869 • *Friedrich Miescher took the initial steps in the biochemistry of the nucleus by separating from cell nuclei obtained from pus and salmon sperm a curious material that he called "nuclein." Nuclein, he found, consisted of protein combined with a complex acid (nuleic acid). He realized that he had discovered a very interesting material which could have great biologic importance, although appreciation of its true significance was long in coming.*

1875 • *Eduard Strasburger described in great detail the process of cell division in plant cells. He gave the process its name, mitosis or karyokinesis, and also designated its various stages which still bear the names he gave them.*

1876 • *Walther Flemming accurately described mitosis in animal cells and applied the term "chromatin" to the deep-staining material in the nucleus.*

1888 • *Wilhelm von Waldeyer gave the fragments into which the nucleus breaks up during mitosis the name "chromosomes."*

Robert Hooke's drawing of the microscopic structure of cork, and the microscope with which he observed it.

"I took a good clear piece of Cork, and with a Pen-knife sharpen'd as keen as a razor, I cut a piece of it off, and thereby left the surface of it exceeding smooth, then examining it very diligently with a Microscope, me thought I could perceive it to appear a little porous; but I could not so plainly distinguish them as to be sure that they were pores . . . I with the same sharp pen-knife cut off from the former smooth surface an exceeding thin piece of it, and placing it on a black object Plate . . . and casting the light on it with a deep plano-convex Glass, I could exceedingly plainly perceive it to be all perforated and porous, much like a Honey-comb, but that the pores of it were not regular . . . these pores, or *cells*, were not very deep, but consisted of a great many little Boxes, separated out of one continued long pore by certain Diaphrams . . . Nor is this kind of texture peculiar to Cork onely; for upon examination with my Microscope, I have found that the pith of an Elder, or almost any other Tree, the inner pulp or pith of the Cany hollow stalks of several other Vegetables: as of Fennel, Carrets, Daucus, Bur-docks, Teasels, Fearn . . . & c. have much such a kind of Schematisme, as I have lately shewn that of Cork."

Micrographia 1665 • Robert Hooke

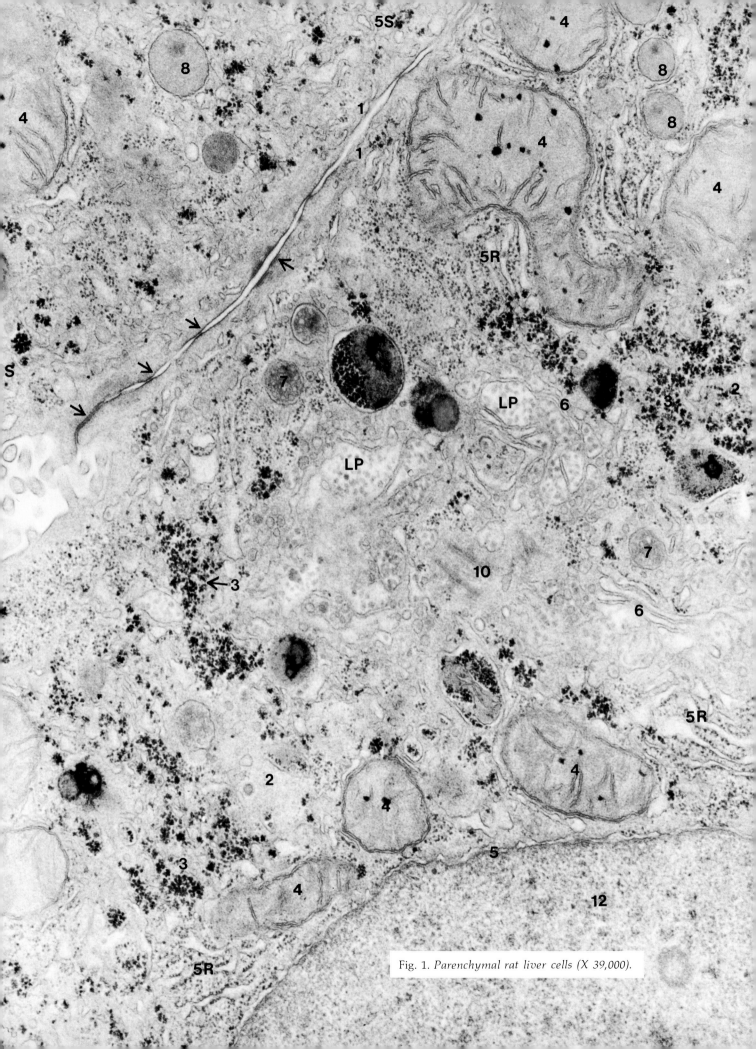

Fig. 1. *Parenchymal rat liver cells (X 39,000).*

Introductory Survey and Table of Contents

Cells are classically divided into two parts, (1) cytoplasm—everything between the cell membrane and the nuclear membrane and (2) the nucleoplasm—everything within the nuclear membrane. Electron micrography has yielded a great deal of information about the cytoplasm and it is with this that the first part of this book deals.

The nucleus has been much more difficult to investigate and has required special techniques to reveal its true structure and function. This will be discussed in the second part of the book.

Before discussing in detail each of the structures in the cytoplasm, a brief look at a typical cell and a quick survey of its contents will be helpful. A liver cell has been chosen for this purpose because a suitable section will show most of the organelles and inclusions in their typical form. These will be enumerated in the order in which they will be taken up in the body of the book.

The illustration shows parts of two hepatic parenchymal cells. The boundary between the two cells extends from just to the right of the center of the top margin of the micrograph diagonally downward and to the left. It ends in a cavity lined with fingerlike projections, a bile canaliculus.

1. *The Cell Membranes* (page 17) of both cells can be clearly seen including *junctional structures* (arrows), which are concerned with holding adjacent cells together and possibly also in intercellular communication (page 19).

2. *The Cytoplasmic Matrix* (page 26) fills the interstices between the organelles. It is a gel-like solution of inorganic substances and various organic compounds from those with only a few atoms to macromolecules.

   A distinction should be made between organelles and cellular inclusions. The former are little organs with a recognizable organic structure; the latter are merely accumulations of a substance produced by the cell or engulfed by it.

3. *Inclusions* (page 26) are exemplified in this micrograph by the numerous glycogen granules.

4. *Mitochondria* (page 28) are perhaps the most conspicuous organelles. They are usually ovoid with numerous shelf-like processes extending from their inner walls. They are the locale of the energy yielding catabolic processes.

5. *Endoplasmic Reticulum* (page 40) is conspicuous in most cells. It consists of many narrow channels often in parallel arrays. There are two types. In one, the channels have small dense bodies outlin-
5R ing them. This is rough endoplasmic reticulum (page 40). Most of the endoplasmic reticulum in this specimen is of this type. That without dense
5S bodies is smooth endoplasmic reticulum (page 41); some is to be seen in the upper cell to the left near the center of the top margin. The nuclear envelope which forms the inner boundary of the cytoplasm is a form of endoplasmic reticulum.

6. *The Golgi complex* (page 46) somewhat resembles the smooth endoplasmic reticulum. It consists of smooth channels and vesicles often arranged in parallel arrays but unlike the endoplasmic reticulum, the arrays consist of only a few units. The channels are not very long and often have enlarged ends which may form vesicles of various sizes. In this specimen the Golgi vesicles are filled with lipoprotein (LP) which looks like grey dots with soft outlines. The Golgi is concerned with the manufacture of secretions and particularly with finishing and concentrating them.

7. *Lysosomes* (page 54) are sac-like organelles containing hydrolytic enzymes and are reaction chambers in which these enzymes can act on their substrate without damaging the rest of the cell.

8. *Peroxisomes* (page 56), like lysosomes, are membrane-lined sacs containing enzymes, in this case enzymes having to do with hydrogen peroxide, either its breakdown or its formation. They characteristically have a uniform consistency save for a central, dark spot called a nucleoid.

9. *Microfilaments* (page 57) are not shown in Fig. 1.

10. *Centrioles* (page 62) are found in most cells and are often conspicuous in liver cells. One of a pair cut lengthwise is shown in this section.

11. *Microtubules* (page 67) are not shown in Fig. 1.

12. The *Nucleus* (page 71) which is the subject of the second part of this book, is discussed under the following headings:

PART I
THE CYTOPLASM

Original 25' cell model.

Cell Membrane

The existence of a bounding membrane for the cell has always been assumed, but its existence could not be unequivocally demonstrated by light microscopy. There was, however, good physical evidence for its existence . . . the swelling of cells in hypotonic solutions, their shrinkage in hypertonic solutions and the escape of the cell contents when the membrane is mechanically ruptured. With electron microscopy of thinly-sectioned cells a membrane was clearly demonstrated, usually about 80 to 100A thick (Fig. 1).

UNIT MEMBRANE

Eventually with high resolution micrographs three layers of the cell membrane were distinguishable (Fig. 2), two electron dense (dark) layers about 30A thick separated by a light space of about 30A. Since this trilaminar structure is seen consistently in various kinds of cells and also in some of the cell organelles, it has come to be considered as a basic structure and is called the unit membrane. The electronmicrographic appearance of the unit membrane has been correlated with the molecular theories of its structure. These concepts were to a considerable extent derived from permeability studies. The great ease with which fat solvents penetrate cells made it seem likely that a lipid was an important constituent of the cell membrane. There were also many reasons for believing that protein was also present, probably combined with the lipid.

By rupturing cells and subsequent differential centrifugation relatively pure preparations of plasma membranes can be made. Erythrocytes have been most frequently used for this purpose. Analysis of these preparations indicates that the lipid is largely phospholipid with some cholesterol-like substances and some neutral fat. Protein was also found. Eventually Danielli and Davson (1935) evolved the concept of two layers of protein molecules sandwiching a layer of lipid molecules between them. As long ago as 1939, I. Langunuir showed that when phospholipid is allowed to spread over the surface of water its molecules all become oriented so that a specific part of the

molecule is in contact with the water. This led to the concept of hydrophilic (water attracted) and hydrophobic (water repelled) groups. Since both the cell's environment and its contents are aqueous the hydrophilic groups are probably directed centrifugally (outwardly). The protein whose molecules are much larger than those of the lipid (very long and much bent about) are most likely intertwined between and attached to the hydrophilic part of the molecules of lipid. There are many more lipid molecules than protein molecules. The electron dense layers are therefore protein molecules attached to the hydrophilic poles of the lipid molecules and the clear area is the hydrophobic portion of the lipid molecules (Fig. 3a). The outer layers of the unit membrane are electron dense because of their affinity for the heavy metals used as stains in the electron micrographs. It is known that such staining materials combine readily with protein, particularly when it is combined with lipid. The diagram, Fig. 3a, shows this molecular arrangement. Experiments indicate

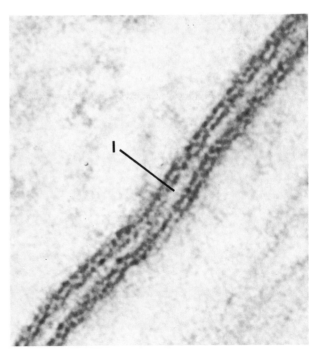

Fig. 2. *Junction between the plasma membranes of two glial cells of the annelid Aphrodite. The three layers of each membrane can be clearly seen. (I) Intercellular space (X 348,000).*

17

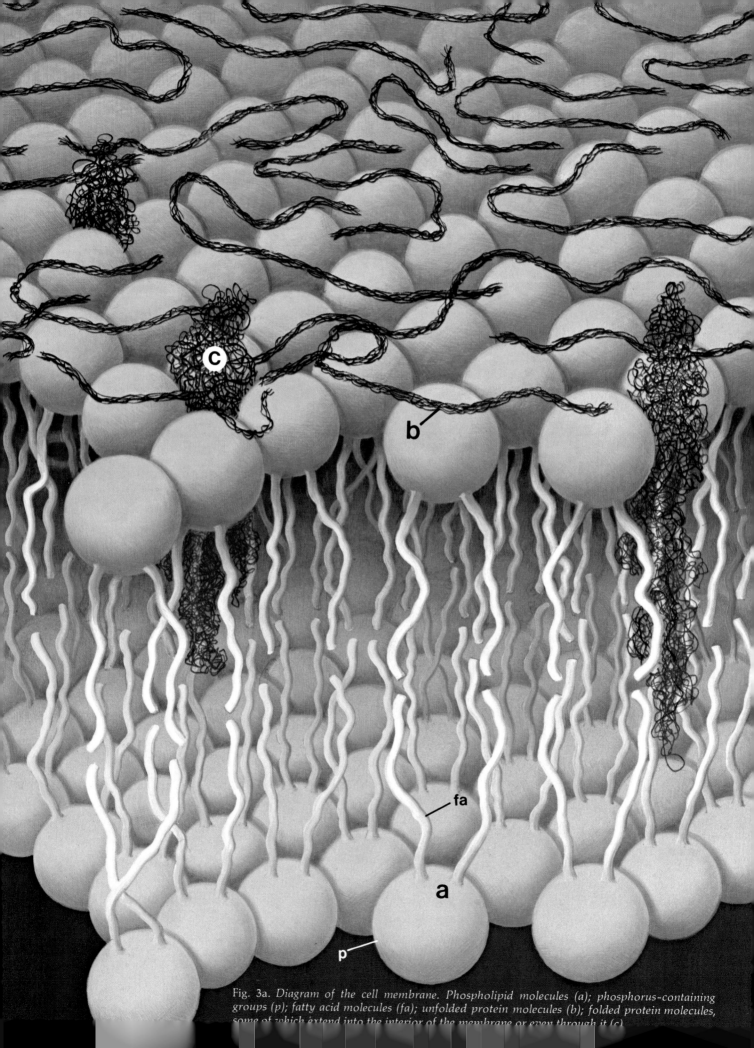

Fig. 3a. *Diagram of the cell membrane. Phospholipid molecules (a); phosphorus-containing groups (p); fatty acid molecules (fa); unfolded protein molecules (b); folded protein molecules, some of which extend into the interior of the membrane or even through it (c).*

that there may be alternative arrangements in certain areas of the cell membrane, at least in certain cells. An arrangement with membrane-lined holes in it would be consistent with some of these findings. A recent theory postulates protein molecules that extend partway or completely through the membrane. These alternate arrangements are also diagramed. This concept of the molecular structure of the unit membrane has been a stimulating one, but is probably going to require modification as information accumulates. For example, the protein on the inner surface may be different from that on the outer and may vary from region to region.

INTERCELLULAR ATTACHMENTS

It is necessary that cells of a tissue be held together and often that cell-bound cavities be tightly sealed. In the days before electronmicrography there was much speculation as to how cells were held together. Interdigitations of the walls of adjacent cells were observed and thought to be important, but there are many cells in which they cannot be demonstrated, so intercellular cements were hypothesized. While interdigitations between the walls of certain cells are conspicuous (Fig. 4) and undoubtedly do aid in holding them together it now seems, that certain specialized structures clearly seen by electronmicrography are much more important.

There are three types of these structures: zonula occludens, zonula adherens and macula adherens. These each have a characteristic appearance in electron micrographs (Figs. 4 and 5). They are very similar in different types of cells.

The one known as the zonula occludens not only joins adjacent cells together but more importantly seals the intercellular space from a channel or cavity such as the intestinal lumen or the lumen of a capillary. In this junction over a narrow region the outer leaflets of the unit membranes of the adjacent cells are actually fused. It is called a zonula because it extends completely around the periphery of the cell in a somewhat meandering line. Serial sections indicate this but it is more

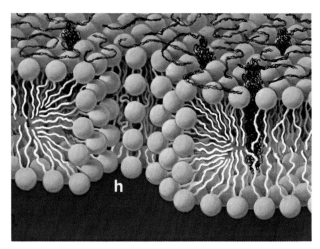

Fig. 3b. *Representation of the cell membrane similar to Fig. 3a but showing holes or pores lined with hydrophilic groups (h).*

graphically demonstrated in surface views revealed by the freeze-etching technique such as those recently obtained by J. P. Revel and D. A. Goodenough. A more graphic term for this technique is "freeze cleaved." The purpose of the process is to reveal the surface appearance of a membranous structure. When tissue is frozen and then broken up, the fractures will occur along natural lines of cleavage which will frequently follow cell membranes or similar surfaces. Replicas are then made by pressing the fractured surface into a plastic substance. The replicas when "shadowed" with heavy metal are observed with the electron microscope. The zonula occludens as revealed by the freeze-cleaved technique can be seen in Fig. 6, which is a view tangential to the surface of the cell. The regions of tight contact, which appear as one or more points in the usual sectional views, are actually interlacing lines.

Another zonula known as the zonula adherens (Figs. 4 and 5) also extends around the periphery of the cell but here the outer leaflets of the unit membrane are not fused but are usually further apart than elsewhere. The gap between them may contain a somewhat denser than usual material and there are areas of dense material on the cytoplasmic surfaces. Its purpose seems to be to hold the cells together.

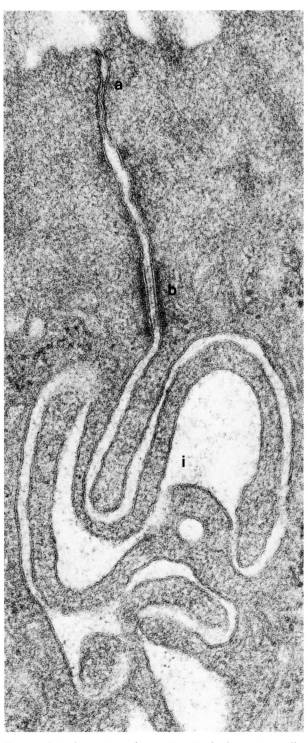

Fig. 4. *Apical portion of two intestinal absorptive cells; (i) elaborate interdigitation between the two cell membranes, each of which is trilaminar; (a) zonula occludens; (b) zonula adherens.*

The third common type of junctional structure is the desmasome, macula adherens (Fig. 5), which resembles the zonula adherens but is a circumscribed structure extending over only a limited area. These structures are distributed here and there over the entire cell surface. They also seem to hold adjacent cells together.

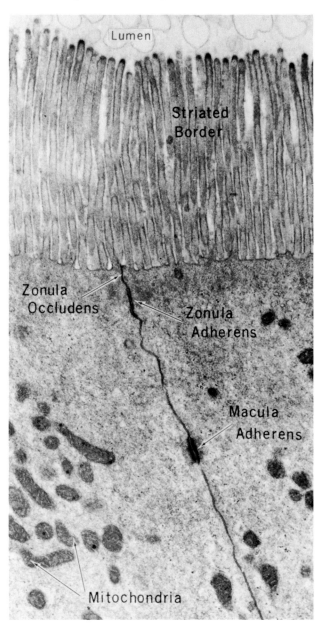

Fig. 5. *Three types of intercellular attachments in intestinal epithelial cells of the hamster zonula occludens; zonula adherens, macula adherens or desmosome.*

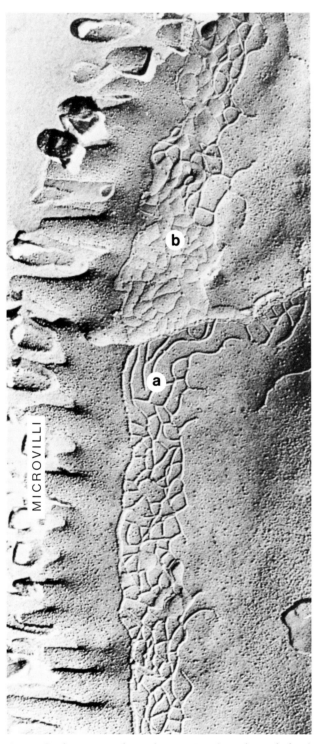

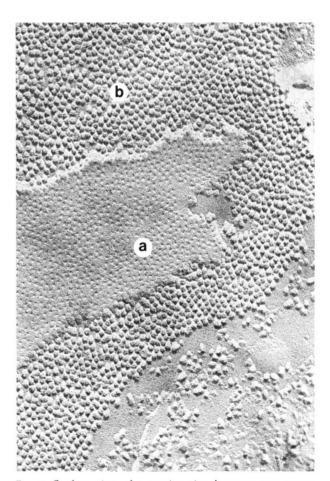

A structure like one-half of a desmasome called hemidesmasome may be found where the plasma membrane makes contact with a noncellular material like a basement membrane.

Recently another type of junction has been described. It was originally thought to be a type of tight junction or zonula occludens but can be shown to be nonoccluding because fluid can be forced past it. It has a somewhat complicated structure. There are polygonal projections from the outer layers of each unit membrane which tend to partially fill but not occlude the space between them. It is called a gap junction or nexus and is an area of decreased electrical resistance be-

Fig. 6. *Surface view of a tight junction (zonula occludens) between two intestinal epithelial cells as seen in a freeze-cleaved specimen. (a) is the intracellular face of the junction and (b) is the extracellular face of the adjoining cell.*

Fig. 7. *Surface view of a gap-junction between two mouse hepatocytes as seen in a freeze-cleaved preparation. The pitted surface (a) is the intracellular surface of one cell and the granulated surface (b) is the extracellular surface of the other cell.*

tween cells and may be important in intercellular communication (Fig. 7). The difference between a zonula occludens and a gap junction is shown diagramatically in Fig 8.

CELL COATS

With appropriate fixation, it is possible to demonstrate layers of material on the cell surfaces. This material, which is often mucopolysaccharide, is probably secreted by the cell. The most conspicuous layer of this type is the basement membrane or basal lamina that epithelia secrete at their basal surface. In Fig. 9 this can be clearly seen. It is interesting that it often does not follow the complex contour of the cell but rather the general boundary of the tissue. This can be seen in (a) the basement membrane of the kidney tubule cells. The basement membrane (c) of the capillary endothelium can also be seen in this section. When this coat occurs elsewhere than the basal surface it is called the external lamina or boundary layer. In certain cells of the intestine it coats the microvillae (Fig. 10a). Here it has been demonstrated to have a fibrillar structure and is called a filamentous coat.

The cell coats are secreted by the cell and are largely composed of mucopolysaccharides. The

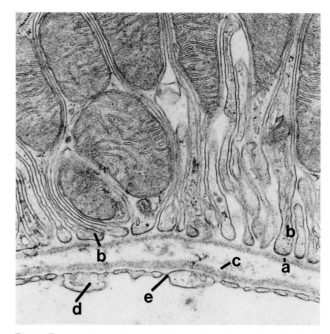

Fig. 9. *Basement membranes of a proximal convoluted tubule of a bat kidney and the underlying capillary. The basement membrane of the kidney cell (a) does not follow the complicated pattern of the protoplasmic feet (b) of the base of the cell but only the general contour. (c) Basement membrane of capillary, (d) endothelial cells, (e) thin membrane probably continuous with outer leaf of endothelial cell plasma membrane. Material going from kidney cell to capillary must traverse both basement membranes and the thin membrane or the endothelial cell itself.*

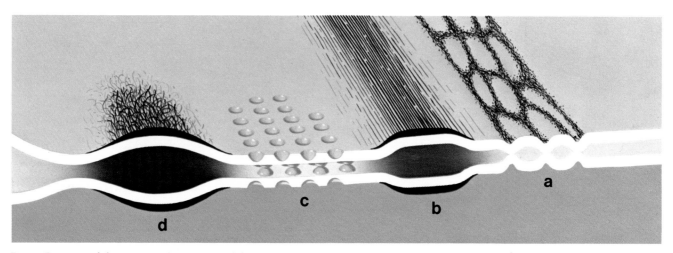

Fig. 8. *Diagram of the junctional structures of the cell membrane. (a) zona occludens; (b) zonula adherens; (c) nexus or gap junction; (d) macula adherens or desmasome. It should be noted that the zonula occludens forms a tight gasket-like barrier. Whereas in the gap-junction or nexus, the dimple-like protrusions are not occlusive. The nexus is permeable not only to ions but also to molecules of considerable size.*

basement membrane may in addition contain some collagen fibrils. Ruthenium red has an affinity for mucopolysaccharides and renders them electron-opaque. It is, therefore, useful for demonstrating the cell coats. In Fig.10b which is part of a cross-section of a capillary both the basement membrane and a thinner endocapillary coat are stained. The stain can also penetrate into the vesicles contiguous with the cell surfaces and enter intercellular junctions. Engulfing of material at one surface, transferring it through the cell cytoplasm in vesicles and extruding it at the other surface is one way material traverses the capillary wall. Penetration of the intercellular junctions is another possibility.

The thick cellulose cell wall of plants is also a type of cell coat.

SURFACE MODIFICATIONS

In certain cells it is necessary that the surface area of the cell membrane be greatly increased. Such cells are usually concerned with the transport of fluid and particles, i.e., absorption or excretion.

The intestinal epithelial cell with its vast array of microvilli on its apical surface is a good example

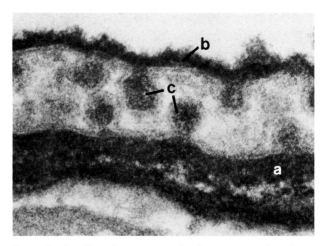

Fig. 10b. *Capillary from mouse diaphragm treated with ruthenium red, basement membrane (a); endocapillary coat (b); vesicles (c).*

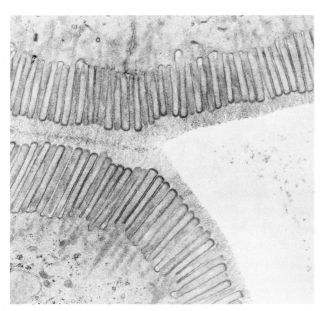

Fig. 10a. *Surface filamentous coat of the intestinal epithelium of the cat.*

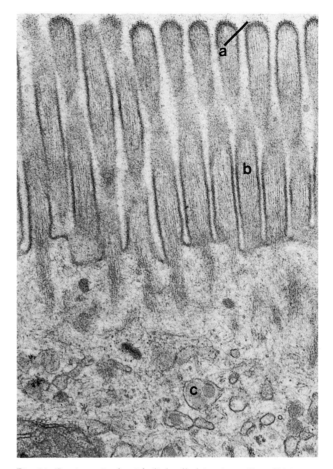

Fig. 11. *Rat intestinal epithelial cell. (a) microvillus, (b) internal fibrils, (c) fat in smooth endoplasmic reticulum.*

23

of this category (Figs. 10a and 11). The microvilli of the intestinal epithelium are a typical and highly developed form of this structure. They are uniform in size and shape and evenly distributed over the surface. While the microvillus is essentially just a modification of the cell surface for the purpose of increasing its exposed area, when highly developed it may show a modification of the enclosed cytoplasm. For example, in Fig. 11 it is easily seen that there are longitudinal fibrillae running the length of the microvilli which extend into the organelle-free cortex of the cytoplasm where they lose themselves in a mat of interlacing fibers which roughly parallels the apical surface of the cell known as the terminal web. A surface view of microvilli in another tissue, the mouse oviduct as revealed by the scanning electron microscope, is shown in Fig. 12.

A much more complicated modification of the cell surface is seen in the basal surface of the cell from the proximal convoluted tubule of the kidney (Fig. 9). Here irregularly shaped projections have been formed to increase the area of this absorbing and secreting surface. They contain mitochondria since energy is required when substances are selectively transported from a region of lower to a region of higher concentration.

Cilia and flagella might also be considered modifications of the cell surface but partake more of the nature of organelles and will be considered later.

NERVE SHEATHS

Perhaps the most dramatic modification of the plasma membrane is the myelin sheath of nerve fibers.

With the advent of electron micrography it is easily demonstrated that the small, slow-conducting nerve fibers originally thought to be naked are actually surrounded by thin cytoplasmic processes of the supporting Schwann cells. How these processes extend around them, one cell often enveloping several fibers, is seen in Fig. 13.

The myelin sheath which encases the rapidly conducting fibers is a highly specialized exaggeration

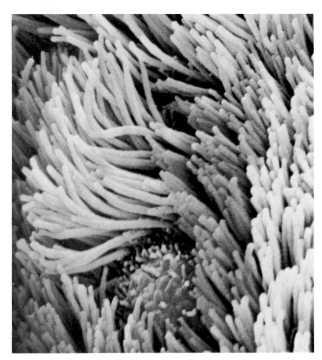

Fig. 12. *Fimbriae (microvilli) of the ovaduct of the mouse, surface view, as revealed by the scanning electron microscope.*

of this process. Here a process of the Schwann cell as it envelopes the fiber becomes greatly thinned out and wraps itself again and again around the fiber, building up many layers. The cytoplasm is completely squeezed out and only layers of the plasma membrane remain. These fuse, producing a sheath of many laminae.

The plasma membrane is not only the retaining wall of the cell that preserves its integrity but an important organelle. It selectively passes nutrients into the cell and metabolites out of it. Presumably its protein components are largely responsible for this. Some enzymatic action may also occur here as the first step in a metabolic process. Various functions of the cell membrane are being actively investigated.

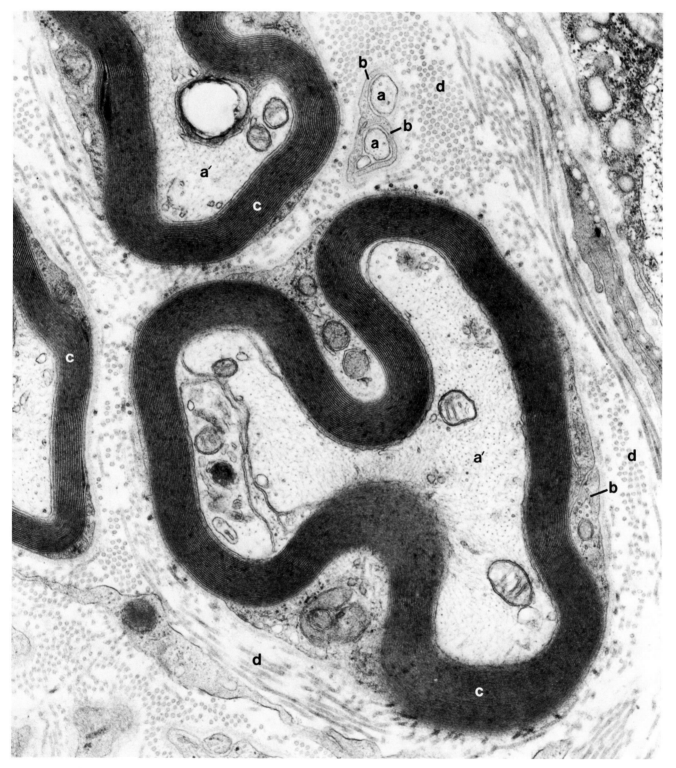

Fig. 13. *Peripheral nerve of a mouse showing myelinated and unmyelinated fibers. (a) slow conducting, and (a') fast conducting nerve axones, (b) processes of Schwann cells, (c) myelin sheath, (d) collagen fibers.*

Cytoplasmic Matrix

In the early days when about the only organelle distinguishable in the cell was the nucleus, it was assumed that most of the material inside the cell or plasma membrane was simple protoplasm, i.e., a solution or gel containing inorganic salts and a mixture of proteins, some of which were enzymes. The various enzymes were thought to be suspended or dissolved in the inorganic salt solution which also contained other crystaloids such as sugars and amino acids. In other words, the cytoplasm was a simple mixture of enzymes and substrates inside a semipermeable membrane.

With the modern work of the electron microscopists and biochemists, this simple concept has disappeared and the cell is so crowded with organelles that there is scarcely any space for any undifferentiated matrix. Still there must be some fluid of gel-like material filling the interstices between organelles which acts both as a supporting medium and a means of communication between them.

This entity is best negatively defined as that part of the cell substance that is not a recognizable organelle. It is also called cell sap or hyaloplasm. It would seem to be a gel-like solution containing inorganic substances and organic compounds of varying molecular sizes from acetates and simple sugars to proteins and nucleoproteins.

To the electronmicroscopist the hyaloplasm is that part of the cytoplasm which has no discernible structure by his techniques. To the biochemist it is the material left in solution after all the particulate matter has been centrifuged out of disrupted and homogenized cells. Much biochemical information has been obtained by disrupting and homogenizing cells and then centrifuging the homogenate at first slowly, which brings down the large particles mostly nuclei and large pieces of cell membrane; then at a higher speed which produces a pellet consisting mostly of mitochondria, lysosomes and peroxisomes; finally, when the supernatant from this operation is centrifuged at still higher speeds for a long time a pellet called the microsome fraction is obtained. This consists of small fragments of endoplasmic reticulum and plasma membrane. It is of interest that the term microsome is now confined to this fraction of a series of centrifugations and does not refer to any specific structure visible in a cell prepared for electron microscopy. Even long centrifugation at high speeds usually leaves many detached ribosomes in suspension. The hyaloplasm is this supernatant minus the ribosomes.

The biochemist relies heavily on the modern high speed centrifuge for the cell fractions which are the starting materials for many of his researches. Indicative of the new concept that most enzymes which act seriatim are adherent in an orderly array on membranous structures so that the metabolic reactions they catalyze take place sequentially, these fractions are more often particulate matter such as mitochondria and fragments of other membranous organelles rather than solutions. Only by keeping enzyme systems intact in this way, can the biochemist observe how they function in the living organism. He may of course, subsequently take them apart to discover their components.

CELL INCLUSIONS

There are a group of objects discernible with both the light and electron microscope which are best referred to as inclusions. They are distinguished from organelles by not having any organic structure although they are occasionally crystalline and are for the most part composed of a single substance. They are immiscible with the fluid of the cytoplasmic matrix and are mostly products of cell activity.

Secretion granules. These are the products of the activity of the endoplasmic reticulum and Golgi complex. They are usually membrane-enclosed and are biding their time until they are extruded at the free surface of the cell (exocrine secretion, Fig. 37a) or into the extracellular space (endocrine secretion, Figs. 30 and 31). Mast cell granules can be considered secretion granules because they act only after discharge from the cell even though they are produced by a wandering cell (Fig. 43).

Lipid droplets. These are globular accumulations

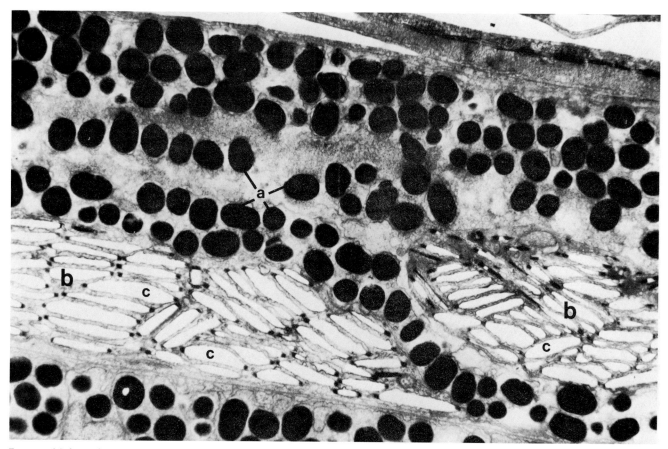

Fig. 14. *Melanophores and iridophores from the eye of a fish (cardinal tetra). (a) melanin granules, (b) iridophores, (c) cavities which in life contained guanine crystals.*

of lipids in the cytoplasmic matrix. They usually have been synthesized in the cell. During starvation lipid droplets may be surrounded by mitochondria engaged in metabolizing the fat for energy.

Glycogen granules. These are small more or less spherical accumulations of glycogen which have been synthesized *in situ* (Fig. 1). They are storage reservoirs of carbohydrate.

Pigment granules. These have usually been made by the cell during its development and are often light screens as in the pigment layer of the retina (Fig. 14). The elongated openings (Fig. 14) also represent another type of inclusion. These spaces hold guanine crystals which by their spacing produce a color due to interference and reenforce-

ment of light waves. They are known as iridophores.

Vacuoles. This is a general term for a membrane-lined globular structure. It is less often used now than formerly and most often serves as a synonym for some more precisely defined structure.

Mitochondria

Mitochondria, unlike certain of the other organelles, were well known before the advent of the electron microscope. In fact, they were accurately described by some of the 19th Century histologists, notably Kollicker and Fleming. Altmann in 1890 discovered a method of staining them. They were described as granules or filaments and were found in most types of animal cells. The many speculations and controversies regarding them are now of historic interest only.

The early electron micrographs of whole unsectioned cells show them clearly, although they give no indication of their internal structure. The early micrograph (Fig. 15) clearly reveals the great length they sometimes have, whereas the modern thin sections seldom show their entirety. Mitochondria nevertheless vary greatly in size and shape not only in different cells but in the same cell in different functional states.

The basic structure of those organelles can be seen in Fig. 16. In general they are ovoid bodies with shelf-like structures extending inward from their walls. On closer examination it is seen that the wall consists of an inner and an outer electron-dense layer separated by a clear space. It has been demonstrated that each of the electron-dense layers of the mitochondrial wall have the trilaminar structure of the unit membrane. The outer layer of the wall is essentially smooth and forms the external skin. The inner layer is much folded, the

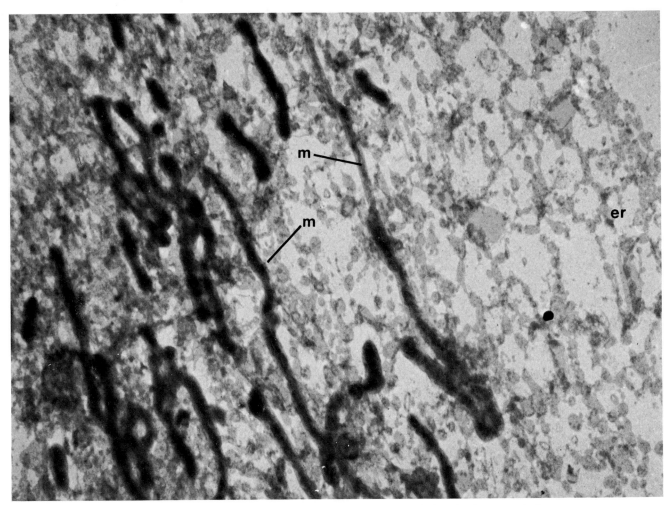

Fig. 15. *Marginal portion of a thinly spread rat tumor cell, (m) mitochondrion, (er) endoplasmic reticulum.*

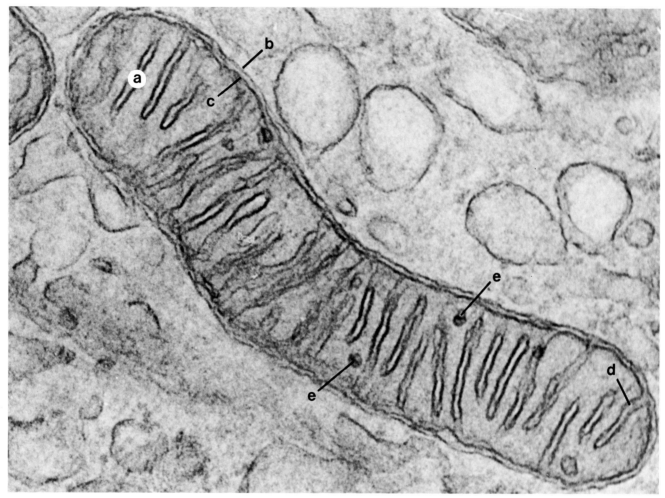

Fig. 16. *Mitochondrion from mouse epididymis. (a) crista, (b) external membrane, (c) internal membrane, (d) outpouching of internal membrane to form crista, (e) granule.*

folds producing the internal shelves which are called cristae. While the cristae are usually flat and shelf-like, they may be round and tubular (Fig. 17 and Fig. 19a). Furthermore, while they usually extend across the shorter dimension of the structure, they may extend lengthways (Fig. 18). Additionally, their structure may change radically with the functional state of the cell (Figs. 19a and b).

MITOCHONDRIAL FUNCTION

The function of the mitochondrion has now been quite definitely established as energy production. This has been accomplished by obtaining rela-

tively pure preparations of mitochondria by differential centrifugation of homogenized cell suspensions, usually liver cells, and studying them *in vitro*. It is not surprising, therefore, that mitochondria are most numerous in those cells whose energy requirements are high such as cardiac muscle cells (Fig. 20). Liver (Fig. 1) and gland cells (Fig. 19a) where chemical work rather than physical work is being done, are also well supplied with mitochondria. The number of cristae per mitochondrion also increases with the need for energy, e.g., cells whose energy requirements are low usually have relatively few mitochondria and there are relatively few cristae in those they do have.

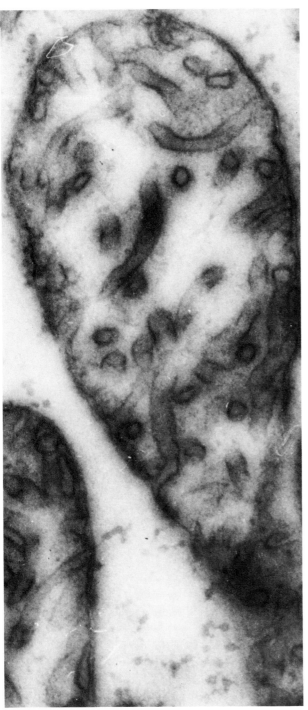

Fig. 17. *Mitochondrion from Paramecium. Here almost all internal structures appear to be tubular. Electron micrograph.*

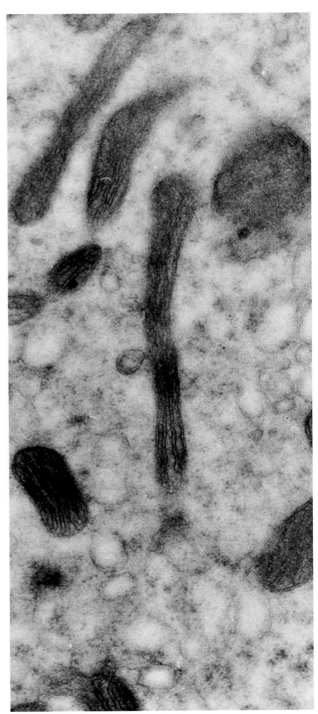

Fig. 18. *Mitochondria from the male germ cell of the snail Otala vermiculata, illustrating their typical internal organization, with lamellae parallel to the long axis instead of perpendicular to it. In the oviduct of the snail, however, mitochondria are similar to those of the Paramecium. Electron micrograph.*

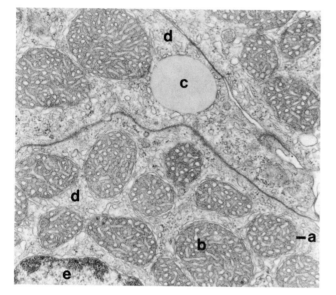

Fig. 19a. Mitochondria in normal zona faciculata cells of the rat adrenal. (a) spherical mitochondrion, (b) tubular cristae, (c) lipid droplets, (d) smooth endoplasmic reticulum, (e) nucleus.

Fig. 19b. Mitochondria in hypophysectomized rat adrenal zona faciculata cells. (a) elongated mitochondrion, (b) lengthways laminar cristae, (c) stained dilated smooth endoplasmic reticulum.

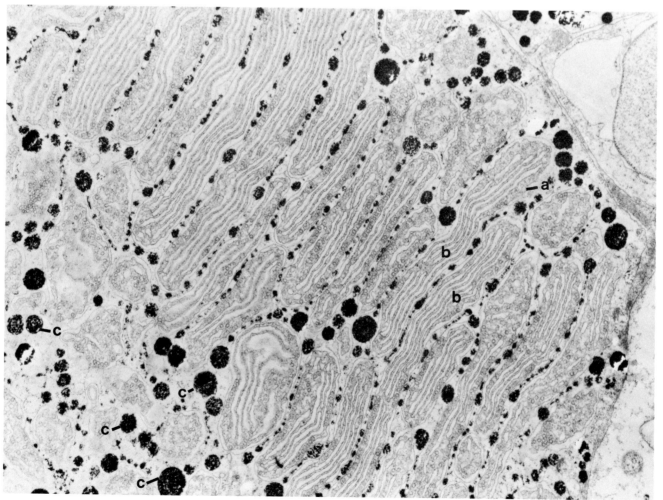

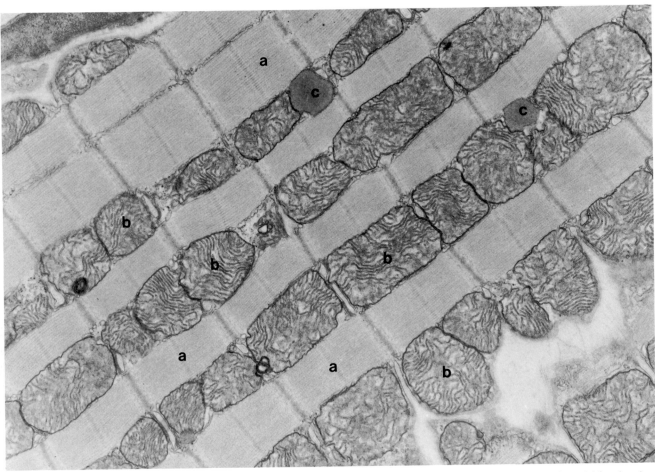

Fig. 20. *Bat heart muscle showing many mitochondria between the myofibrils. (a) myofibrils, (b) mitochondria, (c) fat droplets.*

The mitochondria are particularly concerned with the release of energy from the metabolic reactions of the Krebs cycle. They have been shown to contain the necessary enzymes for this purpose, including those involved in the production of ATP (adenosine triphosphate) from ADP (adenosine diphosphate) by oxidative phosphorylations. Both of these processes are outlined in the diagrams Figs. 21 and 22.

Reference has already been made to the association of enzymes and their coenzymes into orderly arrays so that the steps in the chemical reactions they catalyze can be brought about seriatim. Such associations occur in the mitochondrion, particularly in the case of the enzymes involved in oxidative phosphorylation. These appear to be attached to the inner membrane as can be demonstrated by the fact that even when this membrane is finely fragmented the fragments still retain their ability to perform those reactions. There are also various experiments that indicate that these enzymes are arranged in small unit assemblies, each of which is identical, and that they are quite uniformly distributed over the inner membrane. So far it has not been possible to associate these individual enzymatic assemblies with any electron micrographically recognizable structure. Certain enzymes concerned with the Krebs cycle are either free in the mitochondrial matrix or are very tenuously attached to the membrane because they are found dissolved in the suspending medium when the mitochondria are ruptured. Others are associated

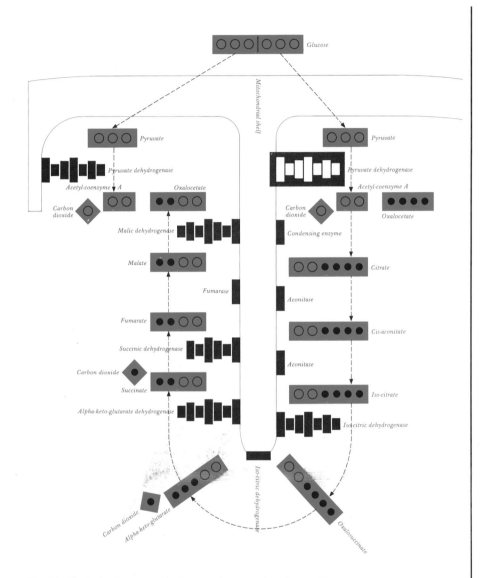

Fig. 21. *Carbohydrate metabolism in the mitochondrion. (Start with the right hand three carbon fragment of the glucose molecule and follow the arrows.) An orderly array of enzymes on a mitochondrial shelf is depicted. Piles of disks represent hydrogen transfer systems; rectangles, other enzymes. Since breakdown of sugar to pyruvate takes place outside the mitochondrion, a three-carbon-atom moiety is shown entering the mitochondrion (bar with three open circles). The carbon atoms of the oxalo-acetate left over from a previous cycle are represented as solid black dots. The complete oxidation of one molecule of pyruvate is shown and the start of a second cycle. The open-circle carbons are lost one by one, but the solid-dot carbons remain to start a new cycle.*

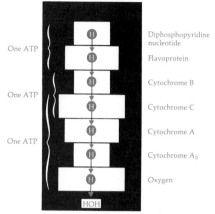

Fig. 22. *A hydrogen transfer (oxidation) system. Diphosphopyridine nucleotide (a nicotinamide-containing coenzyme) removes a hydrogen from the metabolite and becomes reduced. Flavoprotein (a riboflavin-containing coenzyme) then attracts the hydrogen and thereby reoxidizes the first enzyme. The hydrogen then proceeds down the column until cytochrome A is oxidized by oxygen itself. Each passage generates three molecules of adenosine triphosphate (ATP), the immediate source of energy for most vital needs.*

with the outer membrane and some may exist in the space between the inner and outer layers.

The diagrams help visualize the reactions that take place in the mitochondria but it must be remembered that, since they cannot be associated with any electron micrographically recognizable structure, their contour in the diagrams is arbitrary. High power electron micrographs of negatively stained fragments of mitochondrial cristae have revealed small spherical bodies connected to the membrane by thin stems and it was thought that these might be the oxydative phosphorylation assemblies but it turned out that they were instead a phosphorylase which presumably is involved in adding the phosphate group to ADP since a phosphorylase capable of catalyzing the reaction $ATP \rightarrow ADP + P$ can under suitable circumstances also catalyze the reverse reaction.

The conspicuous granules in the mitochondrial matrix (Fig. 16) appear to be storage reservoirs for calcium and possibly other divalent ions and seem to enlarge when large amounts of calcium and phosphate ions have been taken up by isolated mitochondria.

Phase-contrast microscopy of living cells reveals that mitochondria are motile and move actively. They may even break up or fuse with one another. Electron micrography cannot, of course, indicate any sort of motion but does reveal that they may undergo marked changes with the functional state of the cell (Figs. 19a and b). These figures show the appearance of mitochondria from a cell from the zona fasciculata of a normally functioning adrenal cortex and from a similar cell in a hypophysectomized animal whose adrenal cortex, lacking the stimulation of pituitary adrenocorticotropic hormone, has ceased to function. The overall shape of the organelle and the arrangement of the cristae have changed radically. The mechanism of this change is not understood.

MITOCHONDRIAL DNA

It has been known for a long time that not all the DNA in the cell is in the nucleus. A small amount is somewhere in the cytoplasm. It is also known that certain heritable characteristics are transmitted by the cytoplasm and the term "plasma gene" has been coined. It now appears that most, if not all, of this extranuclear DNA is in the mitochondria and, in the case of plants, also is in chloroplasts.

Another peculiarity of mitochondria that has been observed is that they are capable of division. The 19th century biologists who made most of their observations on living material observed both motion and division of mitochondria. In fact, Altmann speculated about the possibility that they might be autonomous organisms capable of independent existence.

It is usually not possible to observe DNA in micrographs of sectioned mitochondria. It can, however, be separated from purified mitochondrial concentrates. When this is done the fibers are found to be the relatively small ring-like molecules such as are characteristic of the DNA of bacteria and viruses (prokaryotes). There are, however, organisms where masses of DNA can be seen in mitochondria. A conspicuous example is the kinetoplasts of certain flagellate protozoa that are blood stream parasites. The example illustrated is Trypanosoma lewisi (Figs. 23a and b) which inhabits the blood stream of rats. A fibrous mass of DNA molecules can be distinctly seen in an otherwise typical mitochondrion; this is the kinetoplast. The DNA fibrils seem roughly parallel and their mass is so great that it displaces the cristae to one side. The DNA in these organelles have the typical ring-shaped double helix typical of prokaryotes (Figs. 24a, b and c). The amount is of course, much greater than in typical mitochondria. The hemoflagellate it should be noted is a eukaryote and its nucleus contains the usual eukaryotic type of DNA.

There are many unanswered questions about the function of the kinetoplast in these organisms. It is shown here as an interesting, albeit unusual, case where DNA can easily be visualized in a mitochondrion. The DNA which it contains is typical of that isolated from other more typical mito-

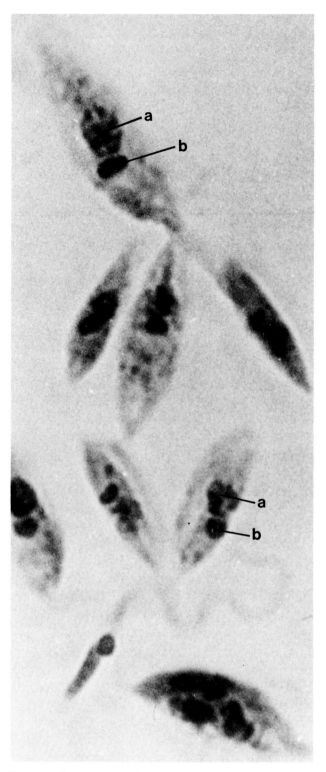

Fig. 23a. *Photomicrograph of Trypanosoma lewisi, Giemsa's stain, (a) nucleus, (b) kinoplast.*

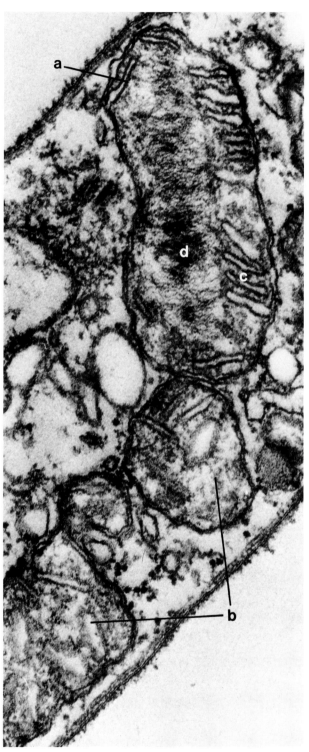

Fig. 23b. *Electron micrograph of a longitudinal section of Trypanosoma lewisi. (a) kinoplast, (b) mitochondrion, (c) mitochondrial cristae, (d) DNA fibrils.*

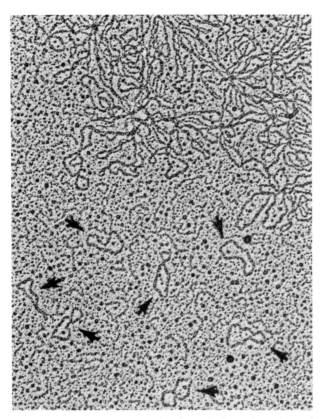

Fig. 24a. *Electron micrograph of DNA from kinoplast of Trypanosoma lewisi showing a lacy mass of rings and some individual rings that have broken loose (arrow heads).*

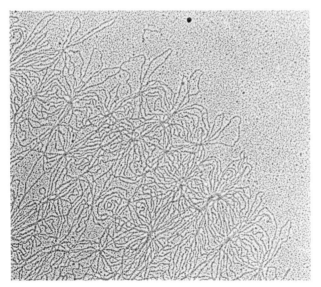

Fig. 24b. *Electron micrograph of DNA from kinoplast of Crithidia acanthocephala. In this species the lacy mass of DNA shows a regular pattern of rosettes.*

chondria. It is interesting that kinetoplasts often divide ahead of the nucleus when the organism divides.

As has been mentioned, division of mitochondria has been observed in light microscopic examination of living cells. It has been difficult to demonstrate with the electron microscope because of the elaborate preparation required. Partition of mitochondria between the two daughter cells has been observed during mitosis. (Fig. 25) A number of experiments indicate that the mitochondria of the daughter cells arise from those received by the partition of the cytoplasm of the parent cell at the time of division. For example, a mutant of the mold Neurospora has been found that cannot synthesize choline which is required for the phospholipids in the mitochondrial membrane. To grow, it must obtain choline preformed from the medium. If this mold is grown for a time in medium containing radioactive choline this becomes incorporated into the mitochondria. If the organisms are then removed from the medium which contains the tracer and allowed to divide, it is possible to demonstrate the tracer randomly distributed among the mitochondria of the daughter cells for several generations. The amount of label per cell decreases with each generation, as would be expected if the mitochondria of the later generations derive from division of those of the parents. Otherwise almost all of the mitochondria of later generations would be free of label and those that were labeled would carry the label in as concentrated a form as it was at the time of labeling.

The available evidence at present seems to indicate that mitochondria come only from mitochondria and are not generated *de novo* by the cell. That mitochondrial DNA codes proteins important to the mitochondria and that these proteins are actually synthesized in the mitochondrion seems certain because ribosome-like particles of RNA, soluble RNA's, the synthesizing enzymes for both RNA production and protein synthesis have been demonstrated in pure preparations of mitochondria. In other words, the necessary apparatus is present. On the other hand, the coding

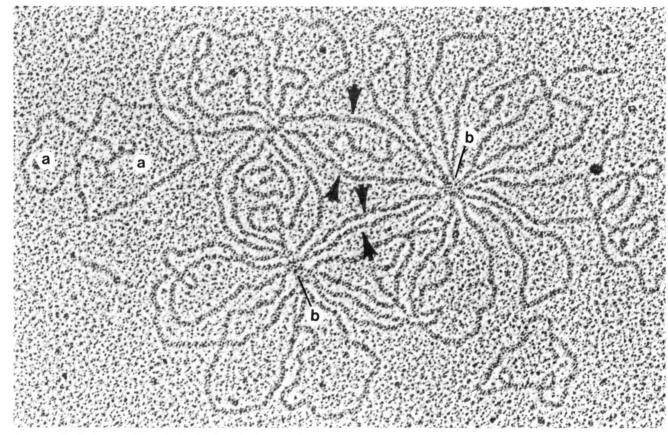

Fig. 24c. *Crithidia acanthocephala DNA at high magnification showing individual loops (a) and rosettes made up of loops (b) and held together by common loops (arrow heads).*

of some of the important mitochondrial enzymes, particularly those of the oxydative phosphorylation system, seem to be coded in the nuclear DNA. At the moment it would appear that the mitochondrial DNA codes some but not all of its proteins.

A recent study by W. J. Larsen in a butterfly, Calpodes ethlius, gives convincing evidence of rapid division of mitochondria in the cells of the fat body shortly after the emergence of the adult from the pupa. The electron micrographs of the

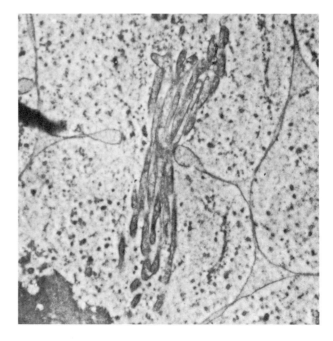

Fig. 25. *Grasshopper testis cell in meiotic division (telophase). Cell wall is reforming and mitochondria are being distributed in approximately equal numbers to daughter cells. Electron micrograph.*

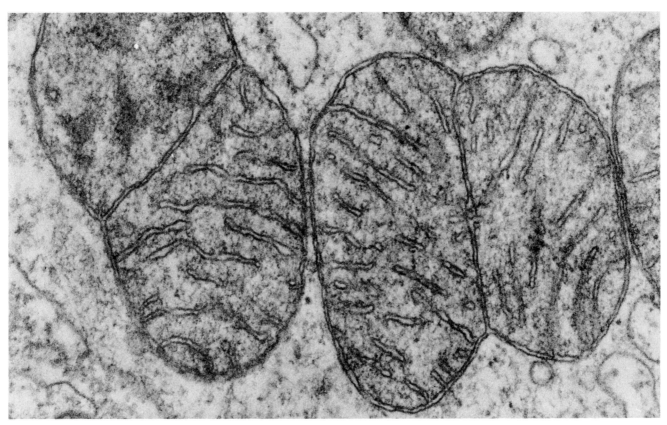

Fig. 26a. *Dividing mitochondria from fat body of the butterfly Calpodes ethlius shortly after emergence of the adult from pupa. The partitions are fully developed and constriction of the walls is beginning.*

mitochondria during this period eloquently document the process. (Figs. 26a and b).

It is interesting that Altmann observed mitochondria divide in living cells with the light microscope and speculated that they might be independent organisms. As a result of the special features of mitochondria and chloroplasts which have just been described, similar speculations are again being made, now in greater detail and with much more convincing evidence. Today's speculations recognize that mitochondria are now very much a part of the cells in which they reside, even though they have a certain degree of autonomy, but that in the distant past they may have indeed been independent organisms. The organism that was to become the future mitochondrion probably was a bacteria-like creature with ring-like DNA such as mitochondria still have but then capable of enough other functions for the organism to exist

independently. This little organism in the course of time made contact with a more highly evolved creature who was not only physically larger but had a more complicated metabolism and means of reproduction. Its DNA was probably already divided into chromosomes and confined in a nucleus.

At this late date it is probably impossible even for the most devoted Freudian to conger up the motivations of these two organisms on their first momentous encounter. Was the smaller intent on insiduously parasitizing the larger? Was the larger possessed, as a result of frustration, of some perverted desire for conjugation, or was he just hungry? If we adopt the first view, the would-be parasite found he could not take over the reins of control, multiply endlessly and thereby destroy his host and, if sufficiently successful, himself also. He did however, find that it was comfortable inside his

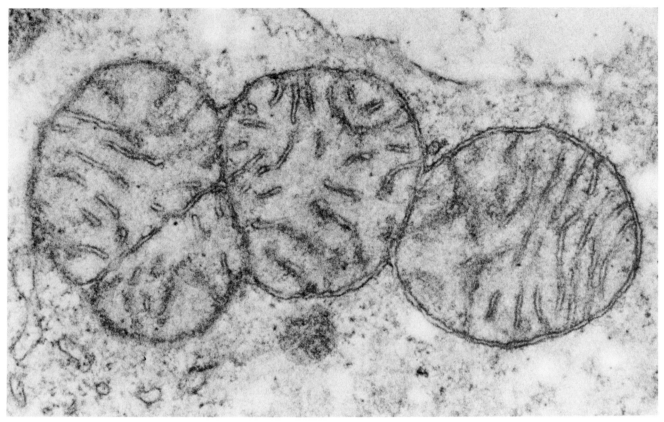

Fig. 26b. *A mitochondrion of Calpodes ethlius showing three stages of division. Earliest stage is at left and almost complete separation at right.*

host and that his host did provide some of those necessary products that he was finding troublesome to produce for himself. Consequently, he could just stop fussing about them. On the other hand, if his host fancied using some of the products the little fellow had learned to produce easily, this was fair enough. Of course, one wasn't going to progress any further this way but what if one did neglect and eventually lose some functions it had taken ages to acquire? It was an easy life and the responsibilities were minimal.

From the point of view of the big cell, the little fellow didn't prove to be a great love or looked at from the other point of view, the little fellow was an indigestible meal but now that he had stopped being irritating, he was useful for performing some of those jobs that had been troublesome to take care of and this made it possible to go on to bigger and better things. In any case, a symbiotic arrangement was established. The big fellow was definitely in charge and the little fellow had become for practical purposes just an organ which the big fellow acquired ready-made and did not have to evolve by the arduous process of mutation and selection. As a result, a long evolutionary stride forward was made by combining the evolutionary accomplishment of two organisms who had taken divergent paths up to their meeting and each had made some advances which the other had not. They might each eventually have independently acquired the valuable assets of the other but the ages necessary to do it were saved by this amalgamation, however unaltruistic the original intentions may have been.

All this could of course, only occur when the big fellow was either still a single cell or had not yet included in his organization, any lymphocytes with feisty ideas about excluding foreigners.

Endoplasmic Reticulum

Endoplasmic reticulum was one of the organelles that was not seen with the light microscope and was first observed by Porter, Claude and Fallam in 1945 as an extensive network occupying the central part of the cytoplasm and not extending into the relatively clear cortical zone. (Fig. 15) When first observed and named, sectioning of cells for electron micrography had not yet been successful. The details of the organelle were consequently not at that time apparent but those early preparations do show its distribution and extent. When ultra-thin sectioning of cells became feasible it was found that the endoplasmic reticulum was made up of interconnecting vesicles and channels, some bordered with small, round bodies (ribosomes) and some smooth-sided. Hence, there are two kinds of endoplasmic reticulum, rough and smooth.

The primary form of the organelle appears to be the rough variety, since the smooth seems to be derived from it by loss of the ribosomes. The amount of each type present varies with the kind of cell and its state of activity. In one form or another, elements of endoplasmic reticulum may extend from close to the outer surface of the cell to the nucleus. In fact, the nuclear envelope is nothing more than a special adaptation of the endoplasmic reticulum.

ROUGH ENDOPLASMIC RETICULUM

The membrane of the endoplasmic reticulum is three-layered like the plasma membrane of the cell. In other words, it has the "unit membrane" structure.

The ribosomes that make this form of endoplas-

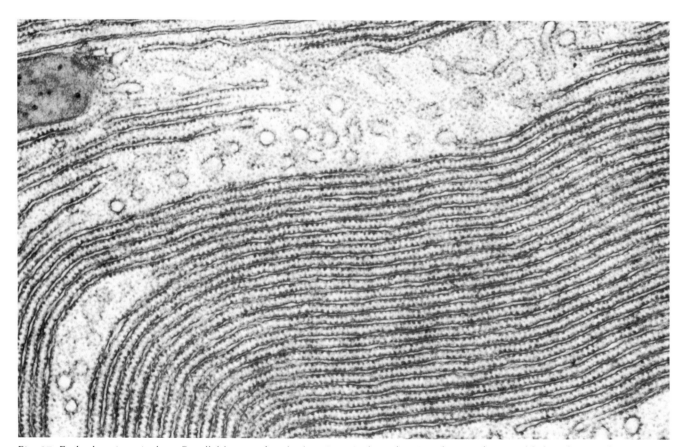

Fig. 27. *Endoplasmic reticulum. Parallel layers of endoplasmic reticulum showing their surface studded with particles of RNA (ribonucleic acid). Electron micrograph of pancreatic acinar cell.*

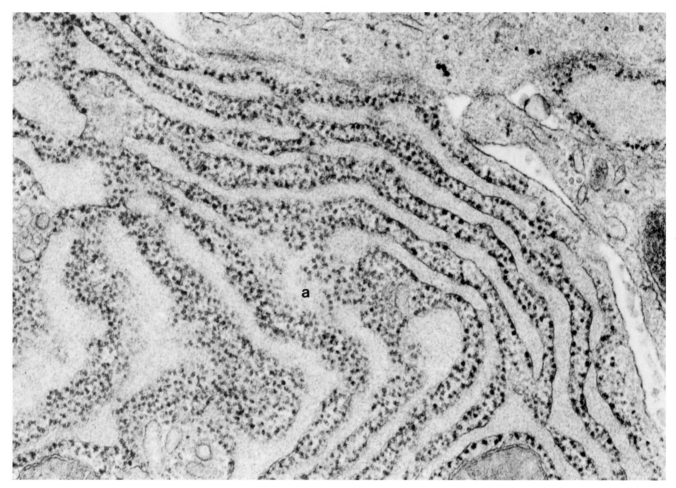

Fig. 28. *Endoplasmic reticulum of a plasma cell showing spiral arrangement of ribosomes on a tangential section, (a).*

mic reticulum rough, lie on its external surface—the face of the unit membrane away from the lumen (Fig. 27). In cross or longitudinal section they appear relatively uniformly distributed. When a tangential or surface view is obtained they often appear to be arranged in repetitive patterns such as loose spirals (Fig. 28).

The function of the rough endoplasmic reticulum is for the most part the synthesis of protein although some nonprotein materials may also be synthesized there. Cells where much protein is synthesized usually have close parallel arrays of rough endoplasmic reticulum, (Fig. 27). In some cells, such as plasma cells whose sole purpose is the synthesis of protein antibodies, a large part of the cell's substance is rough endoplasmic reticulum and accumulated secretion (Fig. 29). As will be described later, the amino acids of the protein are actually arranged and joined together on the ribosomes and then migrate through the wall into the lumen. While there are enzymes associated with the wall, their function is still not clear. Often such a secretion is transferred to the Golgi complex where it is enclosed in a membranous saccule and condensed into a secretion granule. The endoplasmic reticulum also synthesizes materials for the cell's own use.

SMOOTH ENDOPLASMIC RETICULUM

Smooth endoplasmic reticulum closely resembles the rough, except that the ribosomes are absent.

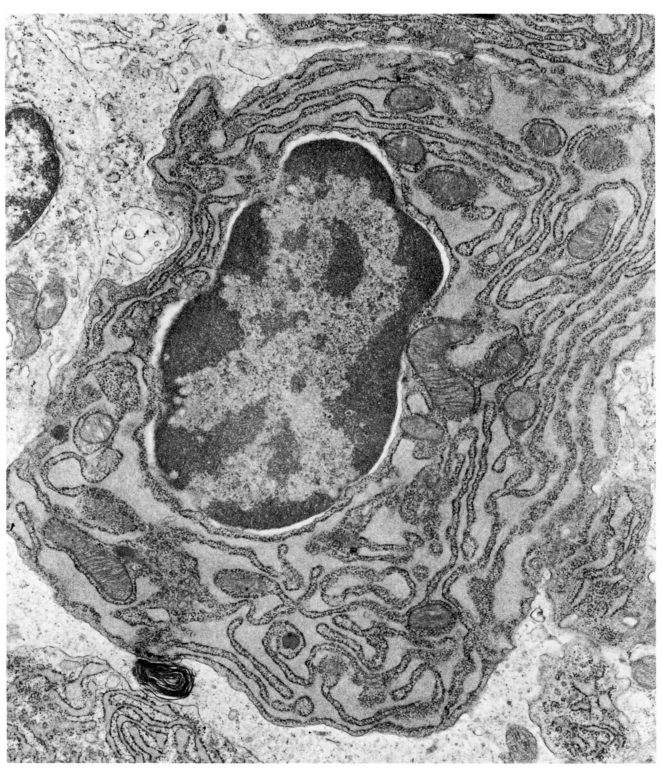

Fig. 29. *A plasma cell from a rat intestine shows a large amount of rough endoplasmic reticulum, with conspicuous ribosomes. The nucleus displays a characteristic arrangement of chromatin, with electron dense masses around the perimeter.*

Possibly large vesicles are less common in the smooth variety. As mentioned earlier, the smooth seems to be derived from the rough. Certain cells can be made to generate large amounts of smooth endoplasmic reticulum rapidly. If such cells are provided with labeled precursors of endoplasmic reticulum membrane, it can be shown that the label first appears in rough endoplasmic reticulum which subsequently loses its ribosomes and becomes smooth.

In some cells both varieties are to be found and in others one or the other predominates. The chemical tasks performed by the two types are different. As has been indicated, the rough endoplasmic reticulum is primarily concerned with protein synthesis. The smooth endoplasmic reticulum is involved more with lipid or fat synthesis. It is, for example, very abundant in liver cells when they are synthesizing and/or storing fat. It appears that fatty acids are absorbed from the

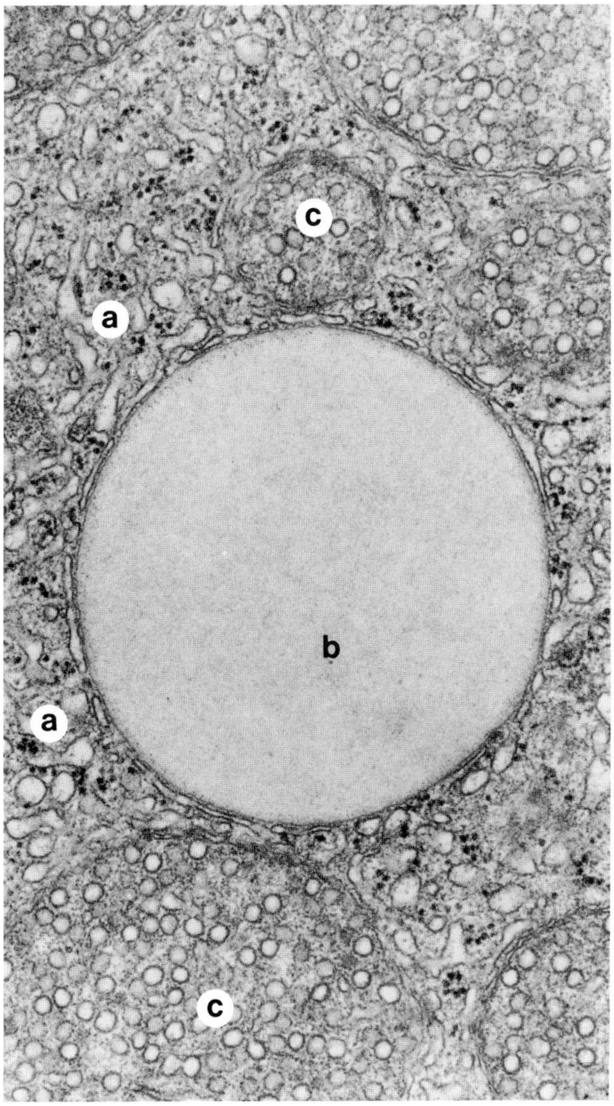

Fig. 30. *Zona fasciculata of a rat's adrenal cortex. (a) smooth endoplasmic reticulum, (b) lipid droplet, (c) mitochondrion with tubular cristae.*

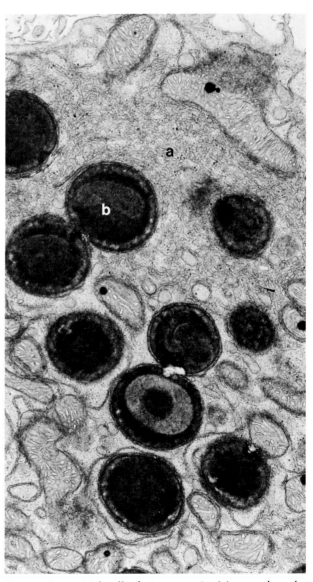

Fig. 31. *Interstitial cell of mouse testis. (a) smooth endoplasmic reticulum, (b) secretion droplet.*

intestinal lumen through the brush border, and are synthesized into neutral fat by the smooth endoplasmic reticulum of the epithelial cells. In any case, it can be demonstrated that shortly after the free fatty acids enter the intestinal mucosal cells they appear as neutral fat in the smooth endoplasmic reticulum (Fig. 11). Smooth endoplasmic reticulum is also prominent in fat cells and presumably is involved in the synthesis of fat from carbohydrate. The organelle is also involved in the detoxification of potentially harmful substances in the liver. For example, a massive increase in smooth endoplasmic reticulum is stimulated in hepatic cells by giving a barbiturate. The steroid hormone-generating cells such as the cells of the zona fasciculata of the adrenal (Fig. 30), or the interstitial cells of the testis are packed with smooth endoplasmic reticulum during their active stages (Fig. 31).

One of the most extensive and highly specialized accumulations of smooth endoplasmic reticulum is in striated and cardiac muscle where it encases the myofibrils and acts to rapidly transport, to and from them, the metabolites incident to muscular contraction. It is here called the sarcoplasmic reticulum. The sarcoplasmic reticulum is closely associated with, but does not open into, the T system—a system of channels extending inward from the sarcolemma at the level of the Z bands which separate the sarcomeres (Fig. 32).

Smooth endoplasmic reticulum is often in close association and may actually seem to communicate with the Golgi complex. Certainly under certain circumstances, vesicles of the smooth endoplasmic reticulum and the Golgi complex are all but indistinguishable. It is indeed, possible to consider the Golgi apparatus a specialized form of smooth endoplasmic reticulum.

NUCLEAR ENVELOPE

Finally, there is a specialized form of endoplasmic reticulum which is present in all cells, the nuclear membrane or perhaps more properly, the nuclear envelope. Except during mitosis, the nucleus is surrounded by a double-layered membrane in every way like a layer of endoplasmic reticulum (Fig. 33). The leaf of this envelope that faces the nucleus is a sheet of typical smooth endoplasmic reticulum. The outer leaf is similar but may be lined on its cytoplasmic aspect with ribosomes and thus resembles rough endoplasmic reticulum. Here and there over the surface of the nuclear membrane there are pores which appear to offer channels of free communication between nucleo-

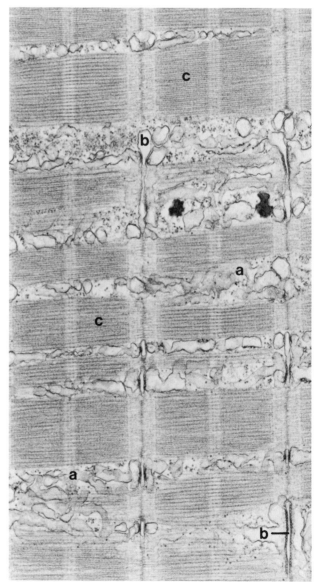

Fig. 32. *Skeletal muscle of a tadpole. (a) sarcoplasmic reticulum, (b) T System, (c) myofibrils.*

44

plasm and cytoplasm. (Figs. 63 & 34a) High resolution electron micrographs reveal that these pores may be closed by a diaphanous membrane. Furthermore, tangential views of these pores indicate that they may be multangular rather than round and that their edges may be framed in a somewhat complex "moulding" called an annulus. No important significance to these complexities has been demonstrated; the pores seem to be functional avenues of communication whereby the various types of RNA formed in the nucleus can pass into the cytoplasm to perform their allotted functions and the metabolites functioning as the triggering substances in the feedback systems that regulate RNA production can enter the nucleus. The idea that they are free and open passageways may, however, be an oversimplification.

In some species there is a fibrous lamina on the inner surface of the nuclear membrane which may give it a quite complex appearance. In amebae proteus it takes on a honeycomb-like appearance (Fig. 34b).

Much work is being done on the structure and significance of the annuli and studies are being conducted to elucidate mechanism of the nuclear-cytoplasmic traffic.

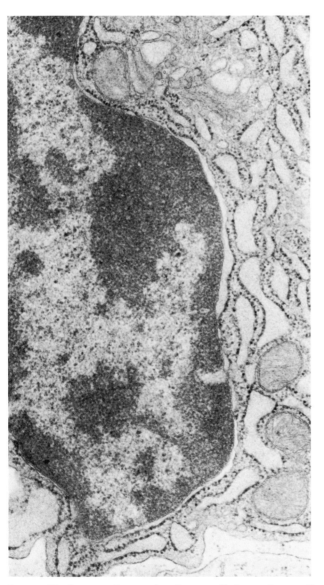

Fig. 33. *Nuclear membrane of a plasma cell. Its nuclear wall is smooth and its cytoplasmic wall is rough, lined with ribosomes.*

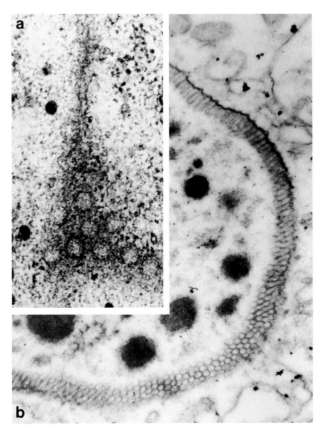

Fig. 34. *(a) Nuclear envelope of insect salivary gland cell showing circular pores where section is tangential. (b) Nuclear envelope of* Amoeba proteus *showing honeycomb-like fibrous lamina on its inner surface.*

The Golgi Complex

Like mitochondria, the Golgi apparatus was well known to the light microscopists appearing as a fine network of fibers which stained black with osmic acid. It is in fact, named for the great Italian histologist Camillo Golgi (1843-1926) who first described it in 1898. It is demonstrable in almost all cells at some time during their life cycle but is much more prominent in some than in others. Its extent also seems to bear a relation to the functional state of the cell.

It was not, however, until the advent of the electron microscope that its highly characteristic fine structure was revealed and demonstration of its function has come only in recent years.

Since the fixation and staining techniques necessary to reveal the Golgi complex gave rather inconsistent results there was much controversy about the significance of Golgi's discovery. Many felt that the structure was an artifact and did not exist in the living cell.

The early electron micrographs, however, consistently showed a characteristic array of cysternae and vesicles in the position where the Golgi complex would be expected and subsequently consistent staining of it has been possible by using stains that react with certain enzymes (phosphatazes) it contains. It was not long after the advent of the electron microscope that it was established that it is not only a real structure but the same one observed by the light microscopists. It usually takes the form of several layers of narrow cysternae often bent to have a bowl-like form. From the edges of these cysternae more or less spherical vesicles often develop. A Golgi complex of medium size and common form is seen in Fig. 35. This view also shows it in a characteristic position —near one pole of the nucleus and close to the centriole. A much more extensive Golgi complex from the epididymal epithelium of the rat is seen in Fig. 36. This view shows well its typical form. The specimen has been stained with lead to demonstrate the presence of thiamine phosphatase which produces a black reaction product. The characteristic change in form from the outer convex layers to the inner concave layers, polariza-

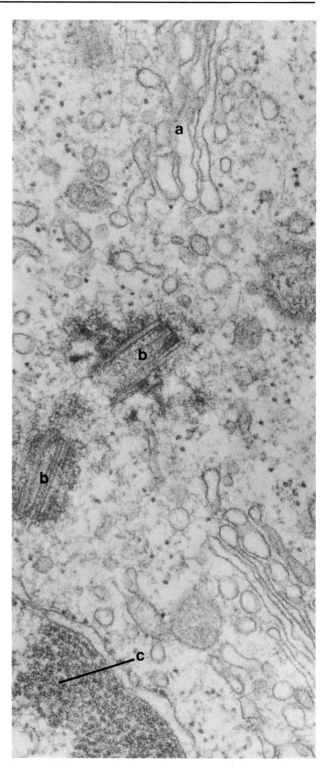

Fig. 35. *Golgi complex in an immature cell showing it in a characteristic position near the nucleus and the centrioles. (a) Golgi complex, (b) centrioles, (c) nucleus.*

tion of form, is shown as well as the polarization of function, appearance of reaction product only in the inner cysternae.

Friend, who took the micrograph, Fig. 36, has also shown that it is only the outer cysternae that stain with osmium. Obviously, therefore, there are pronounced changes in chemistry as one progresses from the outer to the inner cysternae. Incidentally, it was this affinity of the outer cysternae for osmium that made it possible for the early histologists to see the organelle. Staining for thia-mine phosphatase also makes the organelle visible with the light microscope and has been of importance in establishing the identity of the Golgi. The membranous wall of the Golgi closely resembles that of smooth endoplasmic reticulum. If it were not for its characteristic contour the Golgi would be hard to distinguish from this latter organelle.

There are undoubtedly important enzyme systems associated with the Golgi membranes and these membranes seem to furnish the saccules in which

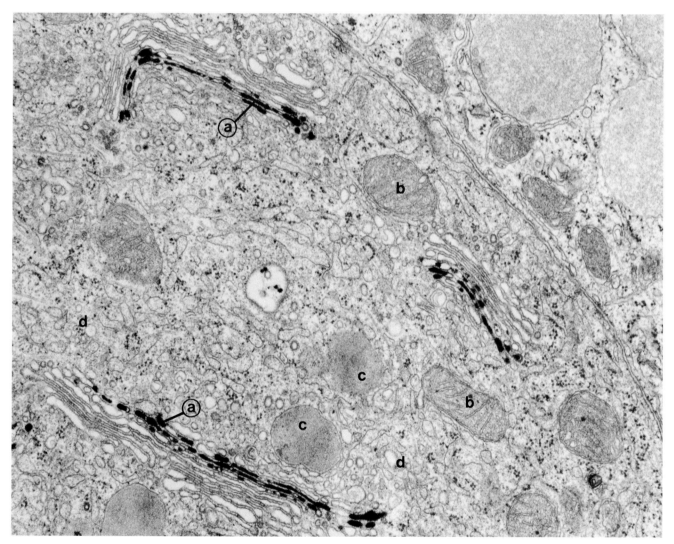

Fig. 36. Golgi complex in epididymal epithelial cell of a rat. Stained with lead to demonstrate the presence of thiamine phosphatase. (a) reaction product in inner concave cysternae, (b) mitochondria, (c) secretion droplet, (d) smooth endoplasmic reticulum.

secretion granules of substances formed elsewhere are often encased. One of the first functions discovered for the Golgi was that of finishing and concentrating secretions made in the rough endoplasmic reticulum. Many of those secretions are protein enzymes which are synthesized on the ribosomes of the rough endoplasmic reticulum and accumulated in its lumen. Subsequently this secretion is transferred to vesicles of the Golgi complex by a process that is not entirely clear but a close relationship has often been noted between endoplasmic reticulum and the outer or convex aspect of the Golgi. The material progresses from the outer to the inner cysternae where it is con-

centrated in condensing vacuoles. Figs. 37a and b, from a pancreatic acinar cell of a rat show this process.

The Golgi's function appears to be much more than just accumulating and concentrating a secretion; important chemical additions seem to be made there. These seem to be particularly concerned with the addition of carbohydrate moieties to glycoproteins, etc. Certain other secretions also seem to be largely made there, such as the cell wall in plants.

Up to this point much of the material has been presented in a rather didactic manner with no great emphasis on the methods whereby the in-

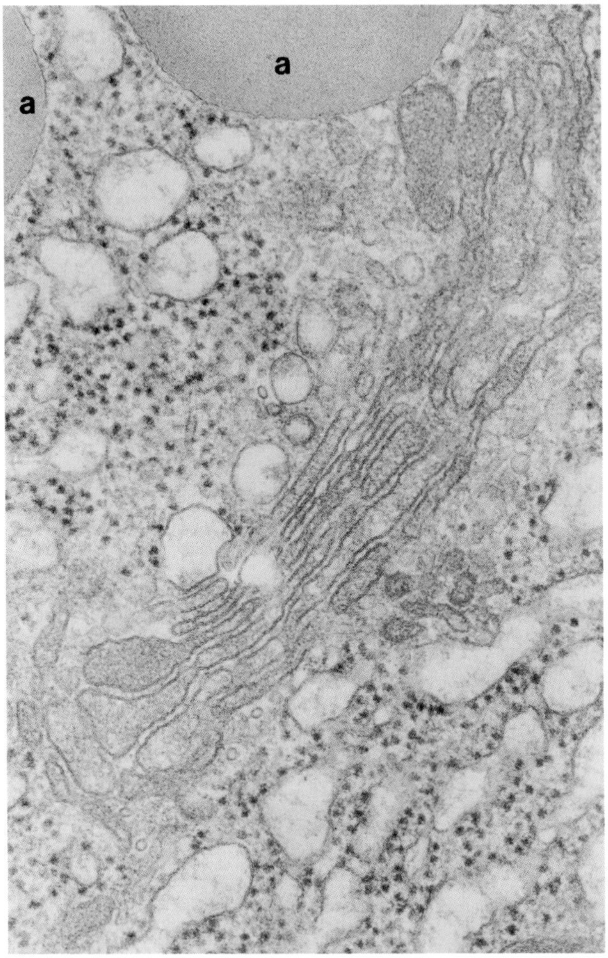

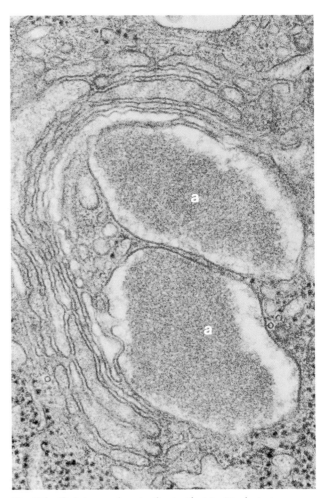

Fig. 37a. *Golgi complex of a pancreatic acinar cell of a rat. The cysternae contain moderately dense material, particularly in the dilated ends. (a) secretion droplet.*

Fig. 37b. *Golgi complex similar to that in 37a but at a somewhat later stage of condensing the secretion. (a) condensing vesicle.*

formation has been obtained. It is, however, desirable that the impression not be given that these ideas are arbitrary or a matter of simple observation. Since a number of interesting and important papers dealing with the functions of the Golgi complex have appeared in the recent literature, one of these will be reported in somewhat greater detail as an example of the methods by which progress is made.

Stains that are specific for a particular substance are very helpful in locating where a substance is in the cell. Perhaps the most versatile type of staining involves the use of radioactive elements —such as ^3H, ^{14}C, ^{35}S, etc. (The superscript before the symbol of the element indicates the atomic weight of the isotope.) They are prepared by exposing the various elements to powerful ionizing radiation. These isotopes behave chemically like normal elements and can be introduced into nutrients or metabolites that will be taken up by cells and used just as ordinary nonradioactive materials would be. Their great advantage as tracers is that the whereabouts of any compound into whose composition they have entered can be determined at any time. This is usually done by fixing specimens of the tissue under study at various time intervals after the radioactive material has been introduced. These specimens are then imbedded and sectioned for microscopic study either by the light or electron microscope. Each section is then coated with a radiation-sensitive (light-sensitive) film and allowed to stand in a dark place for a long enough time for the relatively weak radiations from the isotope to effect the silver halide in the coating. The sections are then photographically developed and fixed. Finally, the section is viewed with the appropriate microscope. Since the sensitive film is permanently attached to the tissue section and is transparent except where it has been affected by the radiations from the tracer, the position of the tracer at the time of fixation can be clearly seen. Examination of specimens fixed at different time intervals after the start of the experiment shows the perigrinations of the tracer.

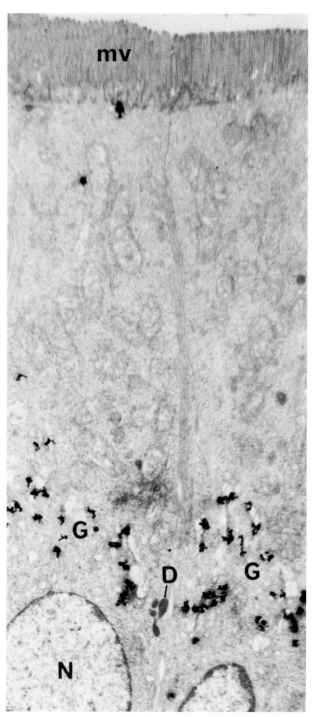

Fig. 38. *Epithelium of the duodenum of the rat 2½ minutes after the injection of fucose (3H). Most of the radioactive material is in the Golgi complex (G); nucleus (N); microvilli (mv); dense body (D), not to be confused with the darker and more sharply defined silver grains indicating radioactivity.*

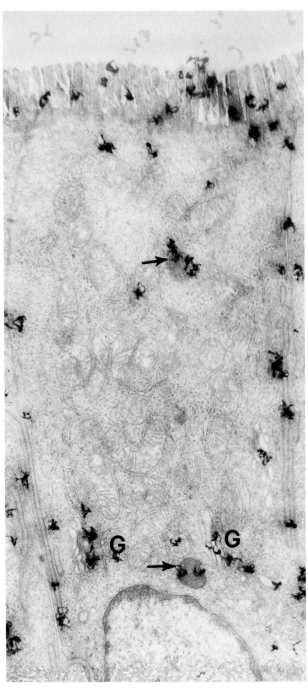

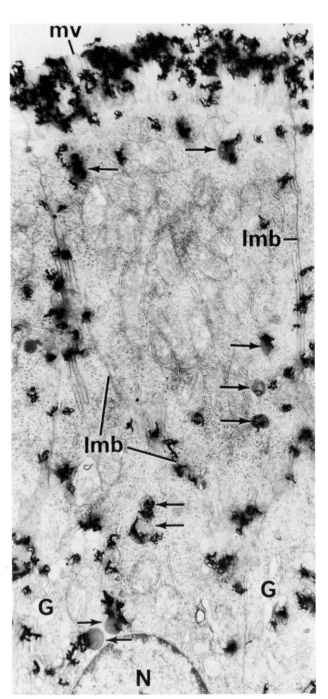

Fig. 39. *Epithelium of the duodenum of the rat one hour after injection of fucose ³H. Label is still seen in the Golgi (G) but is now prominent in the brush border and on the lateral cell membranes and in lysosomes (arrows).*

Fig. 40. *Epithelium of rat duodenum four hours after injection of (³H) fucose. Most of the radioactive material is now in brush borders (mv), the lateral membranes (lmb) and lysosomes arrows.*

It has been demonstrated that the plasma membranes of many cells are covered with a coating which particularly on their free surfaces may appear "fuzzy" (Fig. 10). This cell coat is known to consist largely or entirely of mucopolysaccharides. The purpose of the experiment to be reported is to determine where in the cell this coat material is made. To this end a radioactive sugar, fucose in this experiment, is introduced and its whereabouts determined at various time intervals thereafter. The tissue chosen for study is the columnar epithelium of the duodenum of the rat. The sections were examined with the electron microscope. Under this instrument the exposed silver grains appear like very black, much contorted worms. Within 2½ minutes the tracer is seen in the Golgi complex (Fig. 38) and immediately adjacent area with very little elsewhere in the cell. In these cells this organelle is located just above the nucleus. Very soon thereafter (20 min.) it is also seen in the brush border and to a lesser extent along the lateral cell boundaries. This is seen in Fig. 39, which was taken one hour after isotope injection. After longer time intervals, less and less is found in the Golgi and more and more on the cell surfaces including the basal surface. It does not, however, seem to migrate to the basement membrane (Fig. 40). Except for some found in lysosomes—an organelle to be discussed later, very little label is found elsewhere in the cell.

To further demonstrate the association of the radioactive fucose with glycoproteins (mucopolysaccharides), a relatively thick one-half micron section of duodenum was stained with phosphotungstic acid at low pH. This stain has been shown to be specific for glycoprotein. Four hours after injecting radioactive fucose, it will be seen in Fig. 41 that the labeling is entirely in the stained (dark grey) areas.

Similar experiments were performed previously, using both radioactive glucose and galactose, both of which enter into the structure of the cell coat. With both of these sugars, however, label was found scattered about here and there in the cell. This made less certain the conclusion that the cell

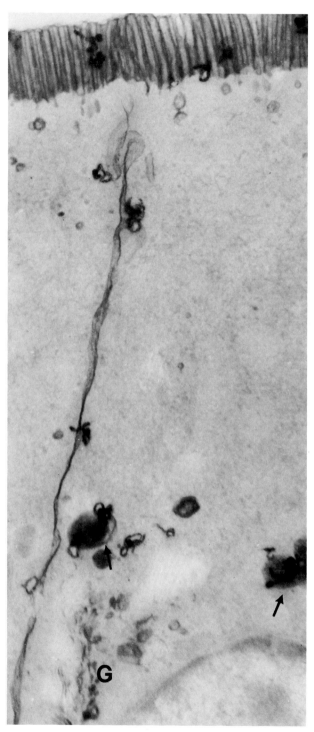

Fig. 41. *Same experiment as in Figures 38-40. A thick section treated with a phosphotungstic acid stain which is specific for mucopolysaccharide. Mucopolysaccharides (dark grey stain) are present in the Golgi (G), the apical and lateral cell surfaces and the lysosomes (arrows).*

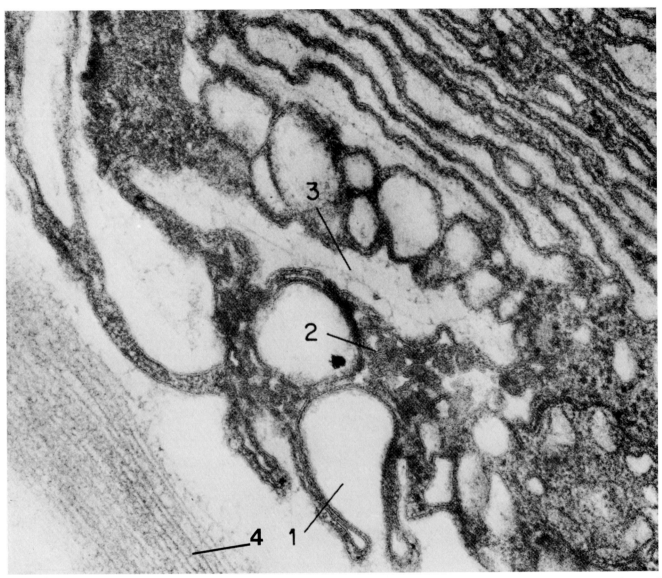

Fig. 42. *Golgi apparatus of the marine algae (Pleurocrysis scherffelii). The closely spaced cysternae are toward the central part of the cell and the wide ones toward the periphery. In the latter are strands of cell wall material (3) which resemble the cell wall proper (4). A cysterna (1) has discharged its material and the remains of collapsed cysternae are seen at (2).*

coat was synthesized in the Golgi complex. It seemed likely that this scattering of the label was the result of the sugars being used in the formation of glycogen. Consequently, fucose which is an integral part of the cell coat glycoprotein but which does not enter into the formation of glycogen was chosen for this experiment and resulted in a more clear-cut result. This experiment was performed by G. Bennett and we are indebted to

him for the excellent pictures we have the privilege of using.

Analogous to the cell coat in animal cells is the cell wall in plants. This is also produced in the Golgi complex or dictasomes as the individual stacks of Golgi membranes are called in plants. Fiber-like elements of the cell wall of a marine algae (Pleurochrysis scherffelii) can be seen in the outer cysternae of the Golgi complex (Fig. 42).

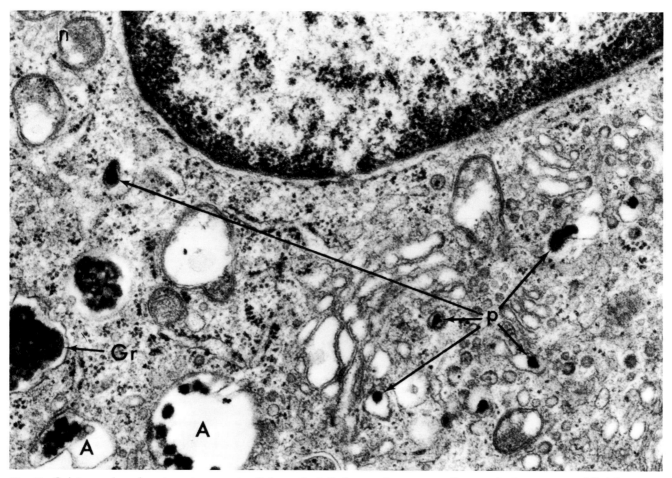

Fig. 43. *Golgi complex of an immature mast cell from the tail of a new-born mouse. Progranules in cysternae of Golgi complex (p); Cysternae with numerous granules in process of accretion (A); mature granule (Gr).*

Similar cell wall elements can be seen in the fragment of the cell wall included in the figures. A still further example of Golgi activity is seen in Fig. 43. Here the granules of a mast cell are being put together.

To summarize, in the case of the pancreatic acinar cell the Golgi is "packaging" and condensing a protein enzyme made in the rough endoplasmic reticulum. It might also be adding some finishing touches to its chemistry. In the duodenal columnar cell it is adding the carbohydrate moiety to the glycoprotein of the cell coat. In the marine algae it is making the cellulosic cell wall and in the mast cell it is elaborating and packaging a mixture of mucopolysaccharides including heparin, bioactive amines and enzymes. Its specialty would seem to be the elaboration of polysaccharide moieties. In some organisms the Golgi complex is capable of participating in the elaboration of very complex structures such as the nematocysts of Hydra.

Lysosomes

Lysosomes are small, membrane-lined sacs which contain proteolytic enzymes, hydrolases. Because the organelle does not have a sufficiently characteristic structure to be definitely recognized morphologically, demonstrating that it contains these enzymes is essential for recognition. Actually the existence of such an organelle as a lysosome was first suspected from the discovery by biochemists that the mitochondrial fraction obtained by differential centrifugation of homogenized cells could be separated into a lighter and heavier fraction. The former lacked cytochrome oxidase but contained a large amount of acid phosphatase. Electron micrographic examination of these fractions showed the mitochondria almost exclusively in the heavier fraction. An organelle containing mostly hydrolytic enzymes was therefore hypothesized.

The obvious purpose of the organelle is to confine these potentially destructive hydrolytic enzymes so that they can perform their alloted function without injuring the cell. The enzymes in the lysosomes are used to digest material which the cell has ingested or, on occasion, parts of the cell itself which have become worn out or in time of need are sacrificed for energy. Gerald Weisman has listed 31 different substances that have been found in lysosomes, not all of them enzymes. Some of the most conspicuous lysosomes are found in phagocytic cells such as granulocytic leucocytes and macrophages. The granules that give the granulocytes their name are lysosomes. The specific granules are typical lysosomes and the large dense granules (Fig. 44) are probably also lysosomal in nature, although they appear to contain a somewhat different assortment of enzymes from the specific granules.

Related to the lysosome is the phagosome, the plasma membrane-lined sac in which phagocytized bacteria or other material enter the cell. Digestion is performed when lysosomes fuse with a phagosome to form what is called a secondary lysosome or phagolysosome. In this way the enzymes contained in the lysosome gain access to the ingested material within a compartment which remains separate from the rest of the cytoplasm. The union of these two organelles is illustrated in Figs. 45 and 46. When living bacteria are ingested they are not killed by the enzymes but by bacteriocidal proteins such as phagocytin within the lysosome.

When a cell has occasion to digest some of its own substance, this is first isolated in a membrane-lined sac much the same as the one formed around ingested material which is then united with one or more lysosomes.

Presumably the enzymes of the lysosome, like other enzymes, are formed in the endoplasmic

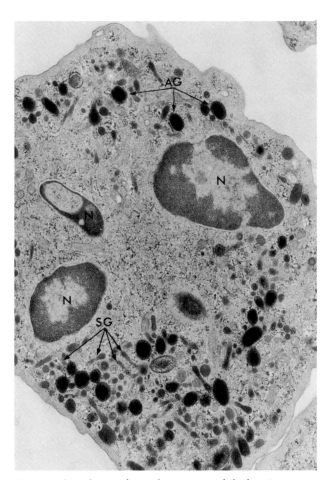

Fig. 44. *A polymorphonuclear neutrophil showing many granules of different shapes. All the specific granules (SG) are lysosomes. The large dense (azurophilic) granules (AG) are also hydrolytic enzyme-containing granules which in addition have been shown to contain peroxidase. They are probably also a type of lysosome. Nucleus (N)*

reticulum. In some cases they may have been formed by a membrane-lined sac budding off from the wall of the endoplasmic reticulum. In many instances, however, the enzymes find their way to the Golgi complex and are packaged there, possibly with additions. It will be recalled that in the experiment described earlier (page 51), lysosomes as well as the Golgi and cell coat were labeled with the radioactive fucose. In this case, obviously the lysosomes received some material from the Golgi complex (Figs. 39, 40 and 41). Lysosomes are of great importance in the inflammatory process, and it has been hypothesized that part of the anti-inflammatory effect of the adrenal steroids results from their strengthening the lysosomal membrane and so preventing the discharge of destructive enzymes into the cytoplasm of the cells.

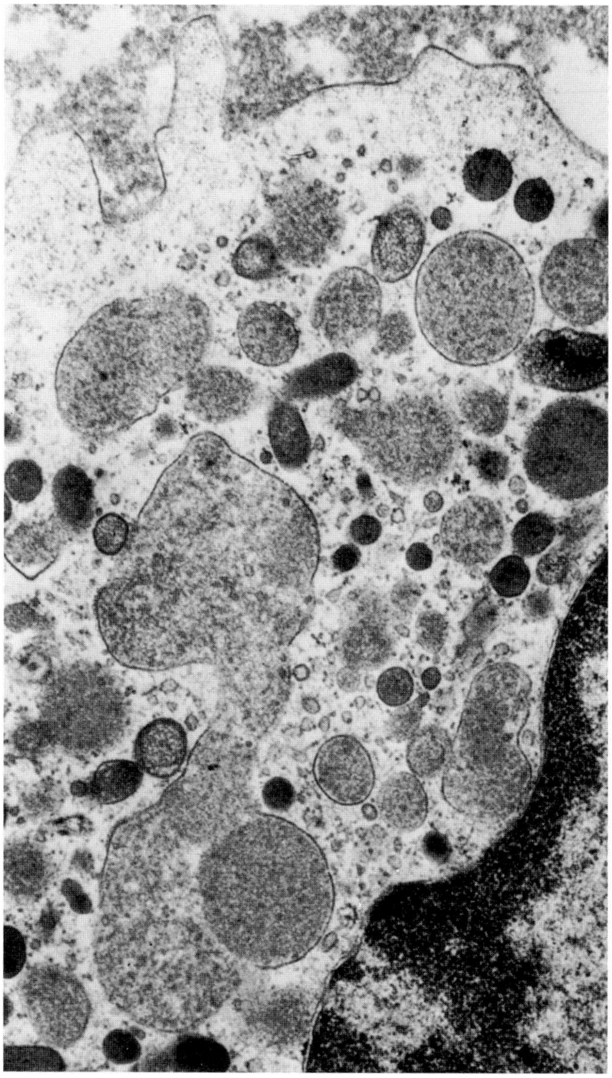

Fig. 45. *Cytoplasm of a polymorph with many lysosomes. One of these is seen joined to the sac in which a phagocytized substance (in this case rheumatoid factor complex) is contained. The membrane of the lysosome has become continuous with that of the phagosome.*

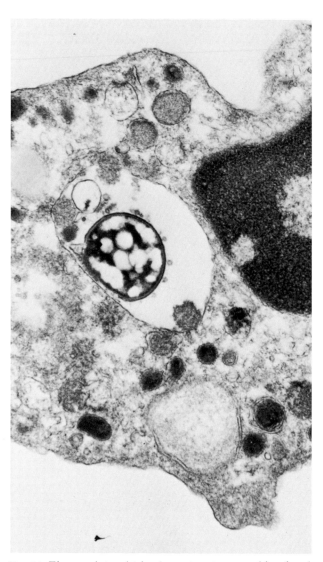

Fig. 46. *The pouch in which a bacterium is trapped has fused with three lysosomes, becoming a secondary lysosome, or phagolysosome. The enzymatic contents of the primary lysosome and their intended prey, the bacterium, are now in a common container.*

Peroxisome

The peroxisome is one of the most recently defined organelles. It, like the lysosome, is an enzyme-containing sac. The enzymes, however, in this case are concerned with hydrogen peroxide either producing it, e.g., urate oxidase or destroying it, e.g., catalase. In addition, depending on the tissue, they usually also contain other oxidases.

The particles are globular and often smaller than lysosomes, i.e., 0.3 to 1.5 μ in diameter. In some cases they contain a central dense body, nucleoid. This latter may have a crystal-like structure in which case the peroxisome usually contains urate oxidase (Fig. 1 and Fig. 47). They are particularly common in hepatocytes and the cells of the proximal convoluted tubules, but are found in a wide variety of other cells in both plants and animals. They have been observed to form in the endoplasmic reticulum and are often seen lying in close proximity to it.

Peroxisomes seem to be concerned with purine catabolism, the breakdown of nucleic acids, and also with the conversion of fat to glucose by the glyoxylate cycle, particularly in plants.

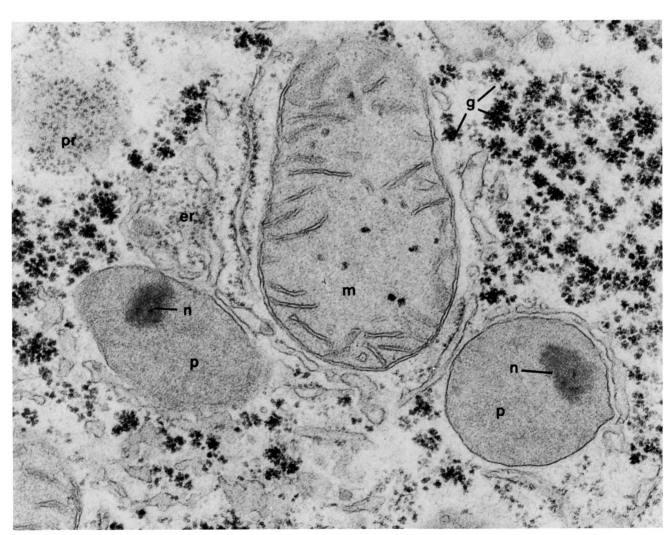

Fig. 47. *Section of rat hepatocyte (X 78,000) showing two typical peroxisomes (p) with nucleoids (n). The striated structure of the nucleoid can be seen in the one on the right. Mitochondrion (m). Endoplasmic reticulum (er) with polyribosomes (pr). Glycogen granules (g).*

Microfilaments

There are present in many cells, microfilaments of various kinds. It has already been pointed out that microvilli contain microfilaments (Fig. 11) that extend into a layer of filaments lying just below the free surface of the cell called the terminal web. These filaments undoubtedly stiffen the microvilli but may have other functions also. Another type of filament found in most kinds of cells are the tonofilaments associated with desmosomes (Fig. 48). The purpose of these also is probably to give mechanical strength and stability to the cell. They appear firmly attached to the desmosomes and then extend into and lose themselves in the cytoplasmic matrix. There is no indication that either of these fibrils are associated with motion.

SKELETAL MUSCLE

The most conspicuous and important fibrils are those associated with cellular motion, particularly in the three forms of muscle found in higher forms, skeletal muscle, cardiac muscle and smooth muscle. While smooth muscle is the most primitive form and presumably the simplest, it has proven the most difficult to study.

Consequently, it is best to start with the most highly developed form—skeletal muscle.

Mammalian skeletal muscle cells are large, cylindrical and multinucleated. This muscle is known as striated muscle because of the conspicuous cross bands observable with the light microscope. With the resolution available with the electron microscope, the finest fibrils observable with the light microscope can be resolved into many much finer filaments but the cross striations persist. In Figs. 32 and 49a for example, a series of repeating striations are conspicuous. The fine muscle filaments are horizontal and the cross striations are at right angles to them. For descriptive purposes the cross striations have been given arbitrary designations. The "z" lines are sharply defined lines and appear to be the termination of one group of filaments. The "z" line or band is in the center of a relatively light band of moderate width. This is the "I" band or isotropic band. Between the "I"

bands is a wide, dark band, the "A" or anisotropic band which is divided in two by a relatively light band, the "H" band. Frequently there is a darker somewhat indistinct "M" band in the center of the "H." The terms isotropic and anisotropic are derived from light microscopy; the isotropic band does not rotate the plane of polarized light and the anisotropic one does. The pattern of bands is repetitive along the fibril. The "Z" bands are considered as the boundaries of the sub units or sarcomeres. Each sarcomere is essentially identical. Much interest has centered in the arrangement of the filaments of the sarcomere and the correlation of this with what is known about the chemistry of muscle contraction. The careful study of high

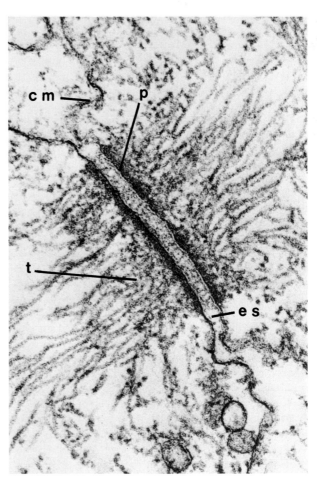

Fig. 48. *Desmosome showing tonofilaments. (c m) cell membrane, (p) dense attachment plaque, (t) tonofilaments, (e s) intercellular space.*

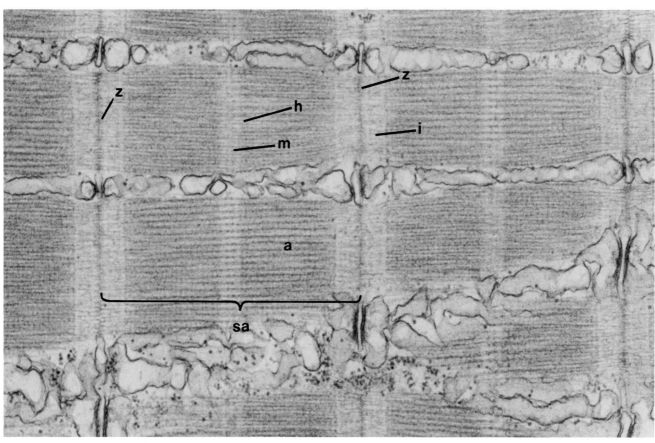

Fig. 49a. *Skeletal muscle from the tadpole.*
Z-line (z); the I-band (isotropic band) (i);
the A-band (anisotropic band) (a); the
H-band (h); the M-line or band (m);
sarcomere (sa).

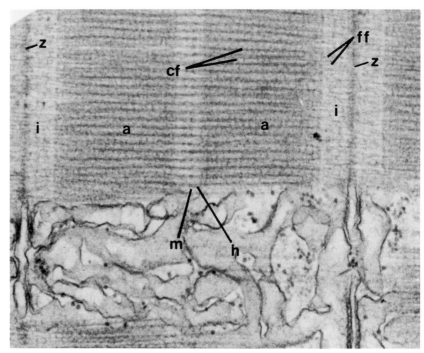

Fig. 49b. *Skeletal muscle at higher magni-*
fication; filaments (ff); coarse filaments
(cf); other designations as in Fig. 49a.

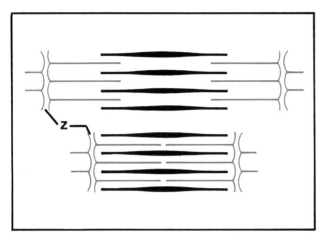

Fig. 49c. *Diagram of the microfilaments of striated muscle in longitudinal section; the relaxed state is above and the contracted state below Z-line (z); fine actin filaments (blue); coarse myosin filaments (black).*

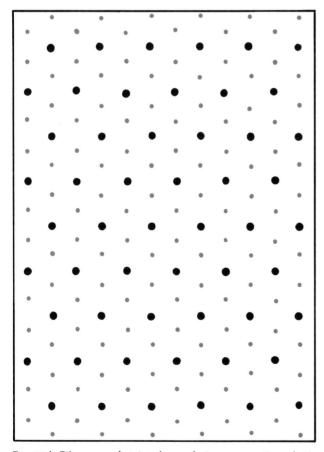

Fig. 49d. *Filaments of striated muscle in cross section. Actin filaments (blue dots); myosin filaments (black dots).*

resolution electron micrographs has shown the existence of two easily distinguishable sets of filaments, a fine set and a coarse set. These can be made out in the enlarged section (Fig. 49b). Here it will be seen that the coarse fibers appear to take their origin in the "M" band, and extend through the "H" band, across both "A" bands to the boundary of the "I" band. It is harder to follow the fine filaments but they can be seen to extend in both directions from the "Z" band across the "I" band and into the "A" band and end at the edge of the "H" band. It is the overlapping of both large and small filaments in the "A" band that make it appear darker than either the "I" where there are only fine filaments or the "H" where there are only coarse ones. The arrangement of those filaments is shown in the diagrams (Figs. 50a and b).

At very high resolutions it can be shown that there are very fine bridges between the fine and coarse fibers. As these bridges form, the fibers are pulled along each other and more completely interdigitate, thereby causing an overall shortening of the muscle. It has been shown that the coarse fibers are myosin—the fine fibers actin. When the bridges form and the muscle contracts, the compound actomyosin is formed. During relaxation the actomyosin disassociates to form actin and myosin. Actomyosin formation is an energy requiring reaction. The energy is obtained by splitting ATP to ADP. It is interesting that myosin is also an ATPase which presumably assists in this reaction.

Before leaving the skeletal muscle, certain other features of its structure should be noted. As was pointed out previously, coarse networks of smooth endoplasmic reticulum can be seen encasing the fibers; these serve to transport the metabolites, incident to contraction. It will be seen that these networks end sharply at the boundaries of the sarcomeres (SR), Fig. 49a. In addition, at the level of the "Z" lines there is another group of channels which do not connect with the sarcoplasmic reticulum, the "T" system (T), Fig. 49a. These channels extend from the plasma membrane of the muscle cell deep into the center of the fibers, and connect there with other similar channels. These channels are thought to transport ions that are tantamount to the spread of the contraction process from the myoneural junctions into the center of the fibers so that contraction takes place almost simultaneously throughout the thickness of the fiber. While they do not show

in this section, skeletal muscle is also well supplied with mitochondria to furnish the necessary ATP.

CARDIAC MUSCLE

Cardiac muscle like skeletal muscle is striated. In fact, the arrangement of the actin and myosin filaments and consequently the striations, are al-

Fig. 50a. *Intercollated disc at the end of a cardiac muscle cell (papillary muscle of the cat). The lower boundary of the muscle cell extends to the right upward along the capillary (c). The zigzag structure of the disc goes upward across two bundles of muscle fibers, jogs right a sarcomere and continues to the upper boundary of the cell which can be followed to the edge of the figure. The longitudinal boundaries of cardiac muscle cells are smooth.*

Fig. 50b. *High power electron micrograph of an intercollated disc. A dense structure corresponding to a desmasome is seen at (a) and a structure corresponding to a zonula adherens at (b). The fine actin fibrils avoid the desmasome-like structure (a) and insert into the zonula adherens-like structure (b). Tight junctions corresponding to the zonula occludens also occur but do not show in the figure.*

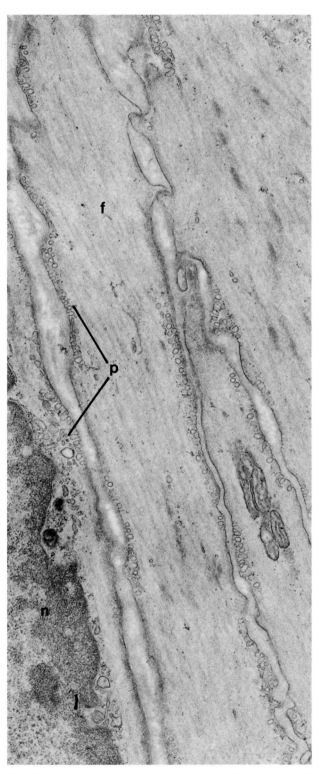

Fig. 51. *Smooth muscle from bat trachea; (n) nucleus; (f) muscle fibrils; (p) pinocytotic vesicles.*

most identical (Fig. 20). Unlike skeletal muscle it consists of individual cells each with a nucleus. These cells are sometimes branched and are attached end to end to adjacent cells by intercollated discs (Fig 50a). The intercollated discs furnish at the same time the boundaries between cells and an anatomical and physiologic connection between one cell and another. It is not only mechanically strong enough so that the ventricle can withstand the tension developed during systole, but the electrical and/or chemical disturbance that initiates contraction passes readily across it. Intercollated discs also show specialized junctional structure similar to those that connect epithelial cells (Fig. 50b).

Cardiac muscle is provided with a sarcoplasmic reticulum (SR) and T system (T) much like that found in skeletal muscle. Its supply of mitochondria is, however, strikingly greater as is clearly seen in Fig. 20. This is required because of constant day and night demand for ATP. Fat droplets are also frequently seen because the heart uses a considerable amount of this nutrient as a source of energy (F), Fig. 20.

SMOOTH MUSCLE

The ordered geometry of internal arrangement seen in skeletal and cardiac muscle is absent in smooth muscle. In most preparations masses of fine filaments parallel to the long axis of the cell is all that is seen (Fig. 51).

Recent work has shown that, as in the other forms of muscle, contraction of smooth muscle results from the interaction of coarse and fine filaments. The coarse filaments are, however, lost in the ordinary processes of fixation and can be demonstrated only by special techniques.

A characteristic feature of the cell membrane of smooth muscle is the marked amount of pinocytoses (imbibition by the formation of invaginations of the plasma membrane which become pinched off and enter the cells as small globules) (P) (Fig. 51).

Centrioles

Ever since the early observations of mitosis it has been realized that there is a body in the resting cell usually located near the nucleus which divides early in mitosis and gives rise to the asters from which the spindle fibers radiate. It was usually known as the cell center or centrisome. Within the centrisome it was discovered that there were a pair of small rod-like structures called centrioles. These were, however, at the limit of resolution of the light microscope. When these centrioles were examined with the electron microscope they were discovered to have an interesting and very characteristic structure.

Fig. 52 shows clearly the typical structure of a centriole in cross-section. It is actually a cylindrical structure whose length is about twice its diameter (approximately 300 x 150A). The wall

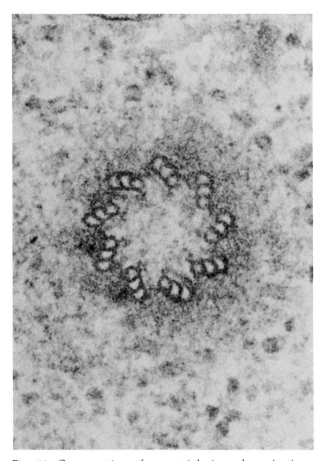

Fig. 52. *Cross section of a centriole in embryonic tissue showing typical arrangement of the triplet fibrils.*

of the cylinder consists of nine evenly spaced rod-like structures, each of which is a triplet composed of three subfibers or tubules so arranged as to resemble the blades of a turbine. Whether these subfibers are indeed tubules or solid structures with an electron-dense exterior layer has not been definitely determined. Two projections from the inner aspect of the innermost subfibers have been described, one directed more or less radially and the other possibly connecting with the outermost subfibers of the adjacent triplet. These are only barely observable in Figs. 52 and 53.

Centrioles never occur singly but always in pairs. The members of a pair are usually at right angles to each other. This arrangement is shown in Fig. 53. This section also shows the characteristic position of the organelle near both the nucleus and the Golgi complex. In this specimen, which is a liver cell, there are two pairs of centrioles, a common occurrence in this tissue, but most varieties of cells have only one set.

Sometimes associated with centrioles are somewhat diffusely dense bodies called satellites (S) (Fig. 53). These are important in connection with systems of microtubules to be discussed later.

BASAL BODIES

Organelles almost identical with centrioles are the basal bodies of cilia and flagella. It should be pointed out that there is no characteristic structural difference between cilia and flagella. In general, cilia are shorter than flagella and more apt to be multiple. Flagella on the other hand are long and either single or few in number; they almost always are concerned with propelling the cell, e.g., the tail of a sperm cell.

It is from basal bodies that the motile cell processes cilia and flagella arise. Those motile whip-like processes either propel the cell through fluid as in the case of protozoa or propel fluid past the cell as in the case of bronchiolar epithelium where they maintain the flow of mucus past the cell surface. In the developing cell the basal bodies are sometimes formed by replication of the centrioles but in other cells they appear to arise

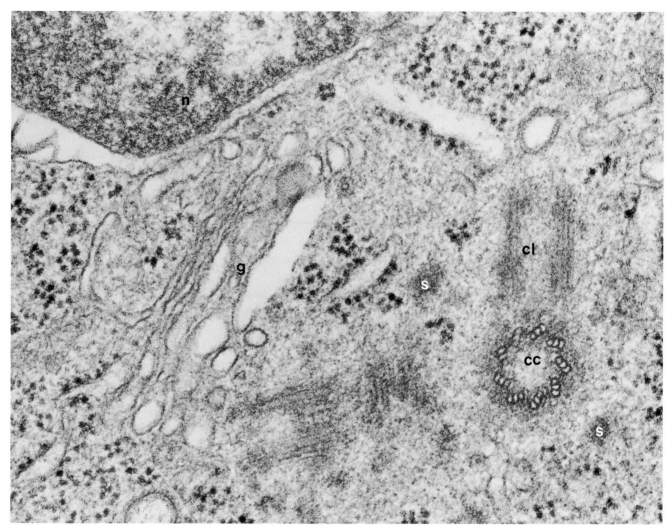

Fig. 53. *Two pairs of centrioles in a rat hepatocyte characteristically placed near one pole of the nucleus and close to the Golgi complex. The characteristic right angle arrangement of the two members of each pair is shown. Satellites of the centrioles are also shown. (n) nucleus; (g) Golgi; (cc) centriole cross section; (cl) centriole longitudinal section; (s) satellite.*

spontaneously from primordia of undetermined origin.

Basal bodies closely resemble centrioles in structure. They are cylindrical structures of similar size and proportion and are composed of the same nine rod-like structures, each of which is a triplet (Fig. 54). The identity of centrioles and basal bodies is further indicated by the fact that the sperm tail may develop from one of the centrioles that functioned in spindle formation during the last division of the spermatid.

In Fig. 54 a cilium (ci) can be seen arising from a

basal body (bb) which in turn is anchored into the cell with rootlets (R). Like centrioles, basal bodies are accompanied by their twin seen at (C) in this figure.

The cilium that arises from a basal body resembles the structure of the basal body. In the figure a diaphragm-like structure (d) separates the basal body from the cilium. It will be seen that the peripheral fibrils of the basal body seem to be almost continuous with corresponding fibrils of the cilium. However, in the cilium there is a central fiber also. In cross-section a further difference in

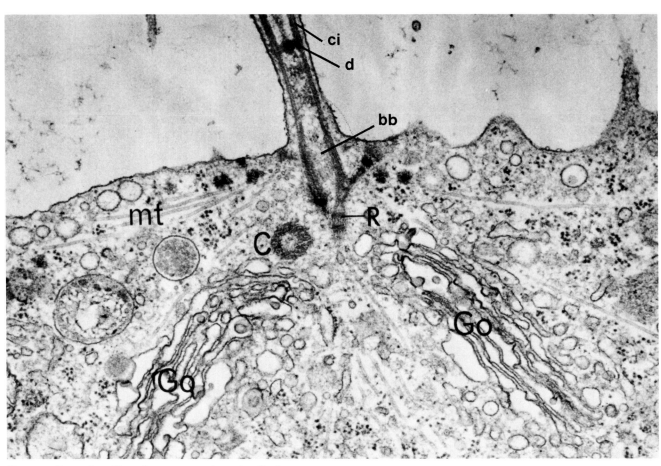

Fig. 54a. *Base of a cilium from an ectodermal cell of a sea urchin (arbacia punctulata) embryo; (ci) cilium; (bb) basal body; (C) twin centriole; (R) rootlets; (d) partition between basal body and cilium; (Go) Golgi; (mt) microtubules.*

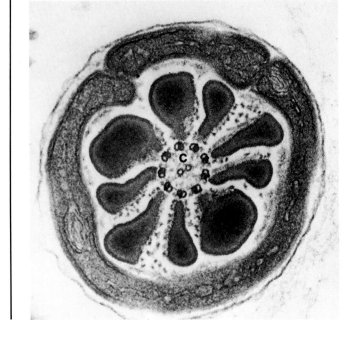

Fig. 54b. *Cross section of the middle piece of a guinea pig sperm tail. It is more complicated than a simple cilium but contains the same central complex (c) of nine doublet fibers and two central fibers. Just inside the cell membrane are the mitochondria of the mitochondrial sheath characteristic of the middle piece of mammalian sperms. The nine pear-shaped structures are accessory fibers which aid in propelling the sperm.*

Fig. 55. *Scanning electron micrograph of cilia on hamster tracheal epithelium.*

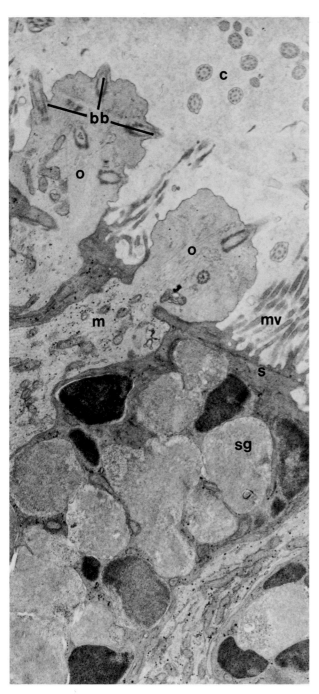

the fibers of cilia and basal bodies is seen; in cilia the fibers are doublets not triplets (Fig. 54b). The central fiber is also a doublet. Surface views of cilia as observed with the scanning electron microscope show them distributed in various ways and usually more slender than microvilli (Fig. 55). While cilia are usually concerned with motion, it is interesting that the sensory cells of smell, taste, sight and hearing are ciliated. The olfactory cells are probably the simplest of these ciliated sensory cells. The peripheral portions of two of those cells embedded in the olfactory epithelium are seen in Fig. 56. These olfactory receptor cells are neurons whose body and nuclei are located midway between the free surface of the olfactory membrane and its basement membrane and are completely surrounded by sustentacular epithelial cells. They send a thin axonal process downward to join other similar axones to form the olfactory nerve. Extending upward is a somewhat thicker dendritic process which extends slightly beyond the surface of the membrane. It is these that are seen protruding above the surface surrounded by the microvilli of the sustentacular cells. The sustentacular cells are filled with large secretion granules of mucus. There are many mitochondria in the olfactory cells. Also, there are the basal bodies of cilia in their protruding ends. These cilia are entirely typical in structure, as numerous cross-sections indicate (Fig. 56). How these cells translate the presence of small concentrations of aromatic substances in the inspired air into nerve impulses that are interpreted in the brain as an odor is unknown but not unspeculated on.

Fig. 56. *Olfactory epithelium of a frog showing ciliated olfactory receptor cells; (o) olfactory receptor cell; (s) sustentacular cell; (bb) basal bodies of cilia; (c) cross and oblique sections of cilia; (m) mitochondria; (mv) microvilli; (sg) secretion granules of mucus.*

Microtubules

As a result of continuously improving techniques, electronmicrographers have in recent years become aware of small tubules in the cytoplasm of many cells. They generally are 200-300A in diameter and of indefinite but considerable length (Fig. 57). This figure shows them in an ectodermal cell of the blastula of Arbacia punctulata and they seem to be radiating from the region of the basal body of a cilium. In general, microtubules are often associated with centrioles and basal bodies. It has already been pointed out that there are somewhat diffuse bodies which may be arranged peripherally around centrioles called satellites. It is apparently these bodies rather than the centrioles or basal bodies themselves that act as terminals for microtubules. This is clearly shown in Fig. 57 which shows a cross-section of a basal body (bb) and a satellite (S), from which many microtubules seem to be radiating.

Sections that are cut so as to include more than one satellite, Fig. 58, show that each acts as a terminal for microtubules.

The diagram, Fig. 59, shows the arrangement of the microtubules in this particular type of epithelial cell. It also shows the arrangement of a basal body, a cilium, the twin centriole of the basal body and three satellites.

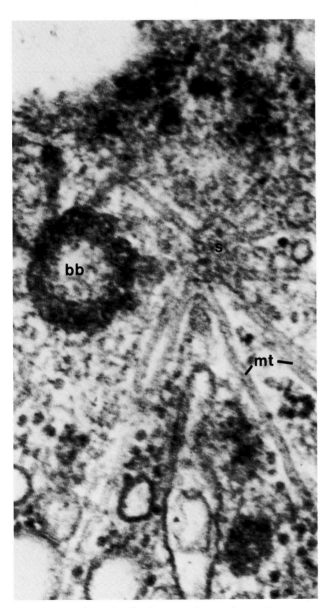

Fig. 57. *Ectodermal cell of sea urchin embryo. Transverse section through a basal body (bb); satellite (s); microtubules (mt).*

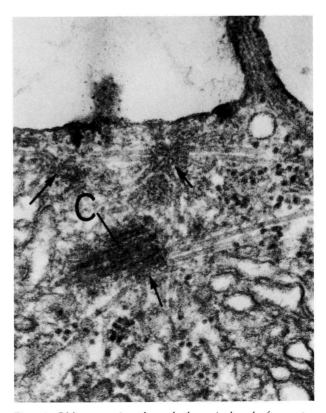

Fig. 58. *Oblique section through the apical end of an ectodermal cell of an Arbacia embryo; (C) twin centriole of a basal body;(arrows) satellites.*

A peculiar property of microtubules is their disintegration under certain physical or chemical circumstances and their spontaneous reformation when normal conditions are reestablished. Reduction of temperature is one way of causing their disappearance in this species.

Fig. 60 is a section similar to Fig. 57 made after the temperature had been reduced to 0° C. for one hour. While a satellite (S) is visible there is no evidence of microtubules. Fig. 61 is a similar

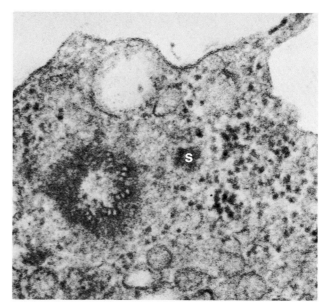

Fig. 60. *Transverse section through basal body of an Arbacia embryo after cooling (0° for one hour) microtubules have disappeared; satellite (S).*

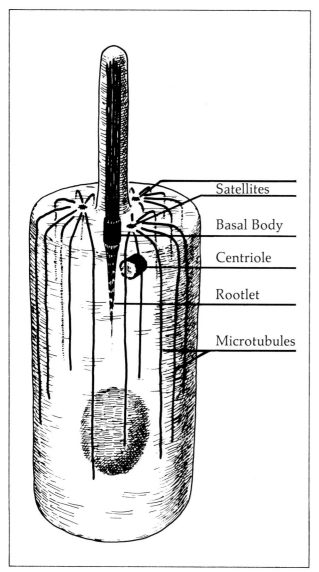

Fig. 59. *Diagram showing relation of basal body of a cilium to its twin centriole, satellites and microtubules.*

Satellites

Basal Body

Centriole

Rootlet

Microtubules

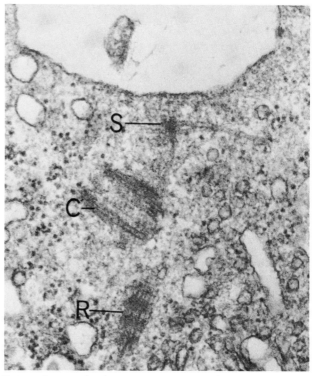

Fig. 61. *Longitudinal section passing near the base of a cilium and through the twin centriole (C) after four minutes of warming. From a satellite (S) microtubules are starting to reform; (R) rootlet of the cilium.*

section after warming for four minutes. A few short microtubules can be seen radiating from the satellite. After eight minutes of warming (Fig. 62), the microtubules are longer.

The experiment of L. G. Tilney and J. Goddard, just outlined, also indicates that as the microtubules build themselves back when the cells are warmed up, they first appear at the satellite and grow out from this as a center (nucleating site). Without such an experiment it would be impossible to tell whether the tubules originated in the periphery and grew toward the satellite or grew outward from the satellite. In this case the latter is true. In other cells and under other circumstances, tubules may grow toward the structure to which they are attached.

All the functions of microtubules are not known. In some instances there is good evidence that they are concerned in maintaining the shape and rigidity of the cell. Their growth and dissolution may be involved in changes in shape such as the production of pseudopods. The tubules in cilia and flagella seem to be concerned with the motion of those organelles.

There is also an association of microtubules with the movement of fluid within cells. They seem somehow to direct such flow although they may not act as pipes but rather the fluid flows along their outer surfaces.

One of the best studied of the functions of microtubules has to do with the division of the nucleus and will be discussed in the next section.

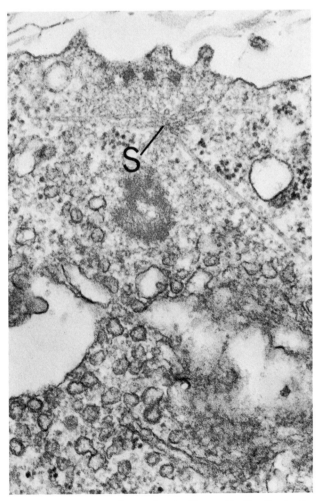

Fig. 62. *A section similar to that in Figure 61 after 8 minutes of warming. From a satellite (S) microtubules are radiating. The microtubules are now longer than those in Figure 61.*

PART II
THE NUCLEUS

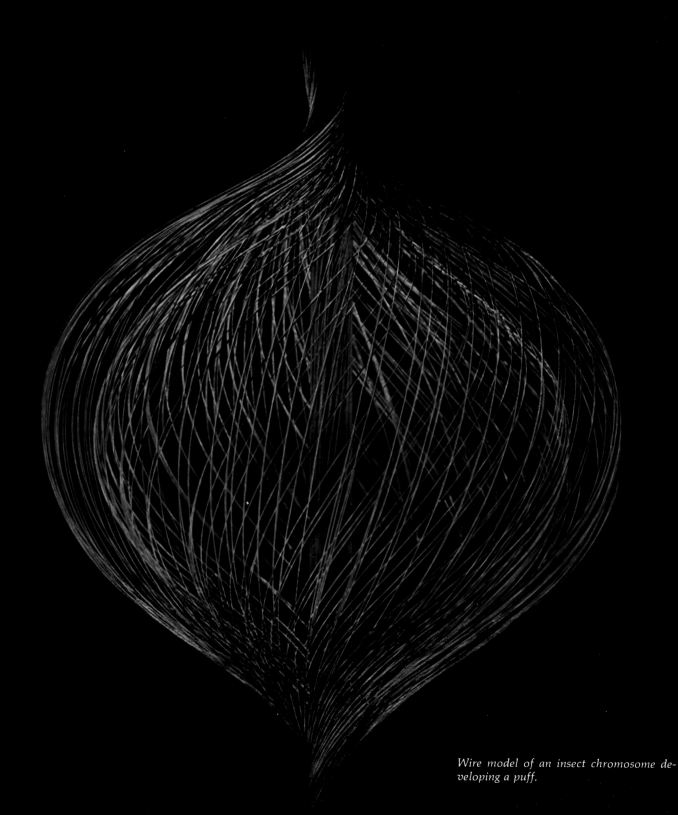

Wire model of an insect chromosome developing a puff.

The Nucleus

Robert Brown, who first observed the nucleus, did so in an unstained specimen and with a single lens microscope. This was in 1831, even before the classic works of Schleiden and Schwann had formulated the cell theory. Any attempt to study nuclear substructure was, however, impossible until after the introduction of staining techniques, which followed the development of the dye industry in Germany during the latter half of the 19th Century.

As staining techniques developed it was discovered that the nucleus characteristically has a pronounced affinity for basic dyes. The substance responsible for this affinity was thought to be a major chemical component of the nucleus and was called chromatin. This concept of chromatin as a principal and characteristic component of the nucleus has persisted and with the introduction of the Feulgen stain that is specific for DNA, it has become synonymous with Feulgen positive material or DNA. Consequently, the nucleolus which stained with basic dyes and was formerly thought to consist of chromatin, is no longer thought to do so because it does not stain with the Feulgen stain and has been shown not to consist of DNA but the closely related RNA with only a small admixture of DNA.

Today two kinds of chromatin are distinguished, euchromatin and heterochromatin. Euchromatin stains lightly, and while the shades may vary considerably, there are no sharply defined masses. Heterochromatin, on the other hand, stains deeply and tends to be in sharply demarcated lumps or granules. The difference is thought to be the state of aggregation of the DNA. In euchromatin the strands are more or less unwound or only loosely twisted together and are in the metabolically active state. In heterochromatin the strands are tightly twisted and folded together and are inactive.

The structures that the light microscopist was able to see in the resting nucleus were the nucleolus and various masses of chromatin which in some cells might assume a fairly characteristic pattern. It was a matter of disappointment therefore, that the electron microscope revealed very little more (Fig. 63).

The one exception is the double nuclear membrane with its fenestrations which has already been discussed. The chromatin masses seen in the light microscope are observable as areas of increased electron density but there is little else except the nucleolus in which some additional detail can be made out.

In Fig. 63 as in most micrographs, the nucleolus consists of a mass of granules (gr) among which is embedded some densely packed fibrillar material (fm). The granules have been shown to be almost entirely RNA but the fibrillar material contains some DNA and also RNA.

It was the study of the nucleus during cell division that made the 19th Century biologists aware of its importance in heredity and which also gave them some concept of its substructure. Consequently, it is now necessary to consider this process

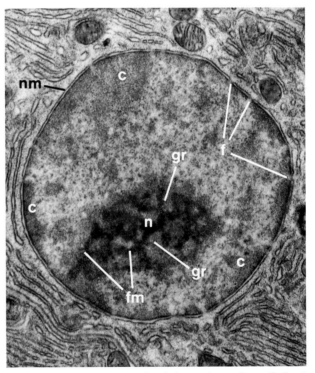

Fig. 63. *Electron micrograph of the nucleus of a cell. (nm) nuclear membrane; (f) fenestrations or pores; (c) peripheral chromatin masses; (n) nucleolus; (gr) nucleolar granules; (fm) dense fibrous masses.*

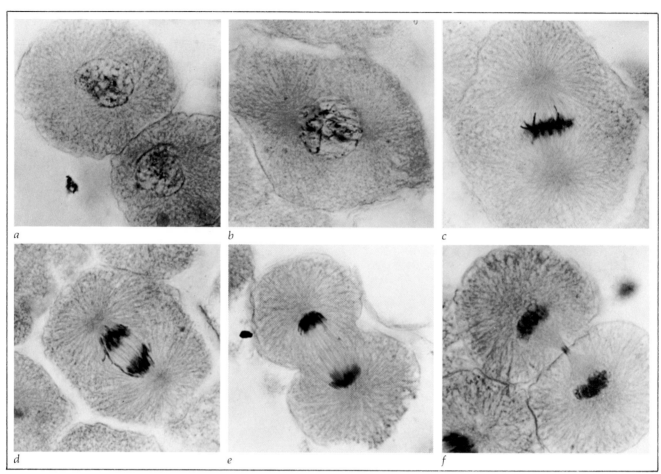

Fig. 64. *Dividing cells in the whitefish blastula. (a) interphase; (b) prophase; (c) metaphase; (d) early anaphase; (e) late anaphase; (f) telophase.*

first as the light microscopists observed it and subsequently as it is currently understood.

MITOSIS

The importance of the nucleus in heredity came in the last quarter of the 19th Century. In 1875 Eduard Strasburger described in great detail the process of cell division in plant cells. He gave the process its name, mitosis or karyokinesis, and also designated its various stages which still bear the names he gave them. About the same time Walther Flemming accurately described mitosis in animal cells and applied the term "chromatin" to the deep-staining material in the nucleus. It was not, however, until 1888 that the fragments into which the nucleus breaks up during mitosis were given the name "chromosomes" by Wilhelm von Waldeyer. The photomicrographs (Fig. 64a-f) represent the process of cell division much as it was described by these classic authors.

a Interphase
The nucleus at this stage is a mass of swollen chromosomes which are tightly packed, not individually distinguishable and stain lightly, probably because they have imbibed water. The nuclear membrane is intact. No centrosome is discernible.

b Prophase
The chromosomes are distinguishable as discrete threads and they are more deeply stained than in interphase, since they are becoming condensed.

The nuclear membrane is disintegrating. Asters are clearly seen at the horizontal poles of the nucleus.

c Metaphase

The chromosomes are concentrated in a line midway between the asters and are discernible as discrete entities. Each, attached to a spindle fiber by its centromere (kinetochore), has split into two chromatids—although this splitting cannot be clearly seen. At this stage no remnant of the nuclear membrane remains. Both asters and spindle are fully formed.

d Anaphase

When the equilibrium is broken by division of the centromeres which have held the chromatid pairs together, suddenly anaphase occurs. The chromatids, now daughter chromosomes, move toward opposite poles, with the divided centromeres leading. The spindle and cell are lengthening.

e Late anaphase

The cell is pinching in two.

f Telophase

In telophase, which is prophase in reverse, the cell's membranes have almost reformed and the daughter cells are connected only by the intermediate body of Flemming. In late telophase the spindle vanishes, the nucleolus and nuclear membrane reappear, and the cell reassumes the appearance of interphase.

THE MITOTIC APPARATUS

In contrast to its disappointing performance in the case of the resting nucleus, the electron microscope has revealed a great deal of new information about the mitotic apparatus. A comparison of Fig. 65a with Fig. 64c will make this clear. Not only is the magnification much greater, but there is very greatly increased resolution. Here the tissue is the testis of the common chicken and the cell is a spermatocyte in metaphase of Meiosis II. A centriole in longitudinal section (c) is clearly seen at each pole. Both of these centrioles at this stage have twins which, however, are not in the plane of the section. The dark diffuse bodies from which the spindle fibers seem to eminate are satellites (s). The spindle fibers (mt) are clearly defined substantial structures which appear to be tubular. That they are indeed tubular is shown in the cross section (Fig. 65b). The structures whereby the spindle fibers are attached to the chromosomes (kinetochores) appear here as two parallel lines of increased density facing toward the poles of the spindle. They are best seen in two locations (k), (k¹); that at (k) is particularly clear.

The structure of the mitotic spindle is now quite clear but what the propelling force is that moves the chromosomes toward the poles of the spindle and how it is applied remains a matter of speculation. It appears not only that the poles to some extent move apart but also that the tubules attached to the chromosomes either shorten or the chromosomes move along them.

Fine bridges have been observed between adjacent microtubules in various types of cells. These have also been observed between the tubules of the mitotic spindle. It is hypothesized that they may be concerned with motion of one fiber past another, in much the same way as the bridges between the thick and thin muscle fibers function in muscle contraction.

There are also spindle tubules that extend from pole to pole without making contact with chromosomes, and fibers that appear to bridge the gap between the separating chromosomes during anaphase. It is these two groups of tubules concentrated by the contracting cell walls during telophase that form the intermediate body of Flemming (Fig. 64f).

The mitotic spindle again demonstrates two of the salient characteristics of microtubules: their ability to form from undetermined precursors when needed and to disappear when their function has been performed, and secondly their association with motion.

It has been known for a long time that the drug colchicine stops mitosis in metaphase. It has recently been found that it does so by causing the spindle fibers to disappear or dissolve. This is a

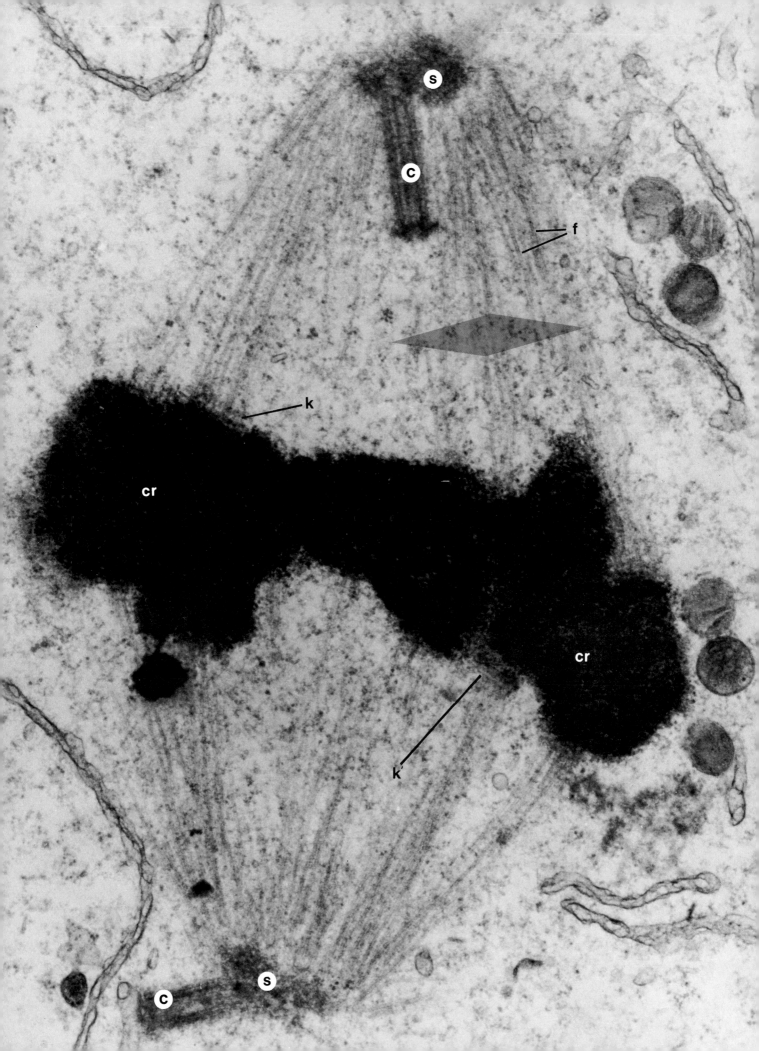

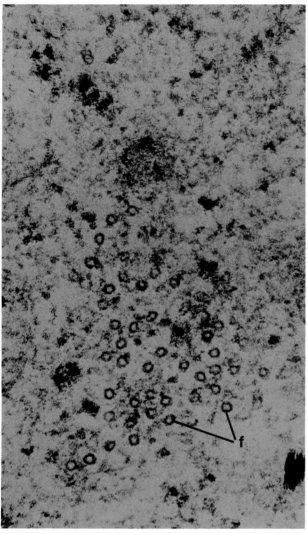

Fig. 65b. *Cross section through spindle showing the tubularity of the fibers (f).*

further indication that the force causing separation of the chromatids in anaphase is applied through the spindle fibers or microtubules.

The author is aware that the mitotic apparatus, derived as it is from the centrioles and their adnexa, is a cytoplasmic structure. Discussing it here in connection with the division of the nucleus is clearer and suits the convenience of both reader and author better than adhering too literally to the distinction between cytoplasm and nucleoplasm.

Fig. 65a. *Metaphase of a spermatocyte of the common chicken in Meiosis II. A longitudinal section of the spindle including one of each pair of centrioles. (c) centriole; (s) satellite; (f) spindle fibers; (cr) chromosomes; (k) and (k') kinetochores.*

Chromosomes

Most chromosomes are small; while they can be clearly seen during mitosis it is only under special circumstances that much detail in the structure of individual chromosomes can be made out. By choosing favorable cells, however, a good deal has been learned about the structure and number of chromosomes in different species. In human cells grown in tissue culture (Fig. 66), it is possible not only to count the chromosomes but to see the two chromatids in each chromosome which will

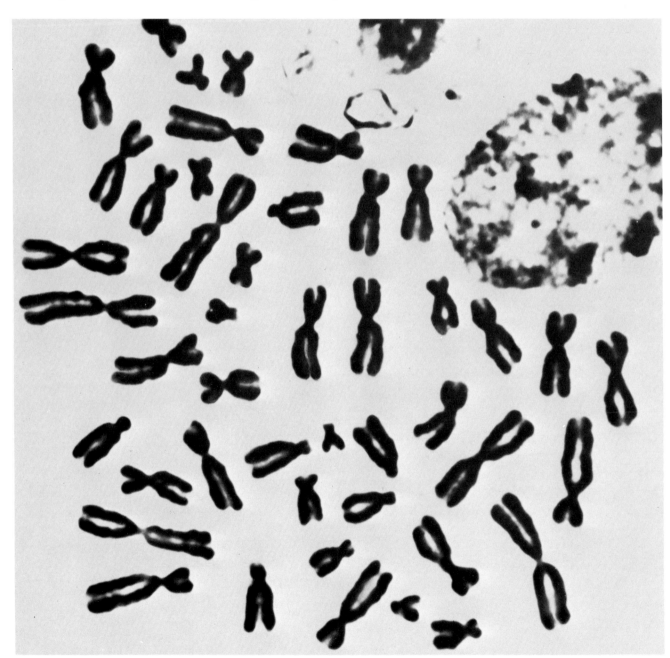

Fig. 66. *Normal human female chromosomes from a cell grown in tissue culture. Mitosis was stopped in metaphase with colchicine, and the cells "squashed" and stained. The two chromatids held together by the centromere or kinetochore can be seen.*

be pulled apart during anaphase. The formation of the two chromatids, involving as it does the synthesis of new chromatin, takes place during the interphase stage because throughout the whole process of mitosis the chromosomes themselves remain metabolically inactive.

The chromosomes are not usually visible as discrete bodies during their metabolically active period because their substance is greatly expanded and completely fills the nuclear space. This is the reason that they stain lightly during interphase. In preparation for the next division the chromosomes start to contract, become more discrete and stain more darkly. As their contraction continues, they tend to twist and sometimes form spring-like helices which can be clearly seen with suitable fixing and staining (Fig. 67). As will be seen subsequently, twisting and curling is characteristic of chromosomal structure.

Of particular structural importance in determining the appearance of individual chromosomes is the centromere of kinetochore, the structure that attaches the chromosome to the spindle fibers and also holds the chromatids together until it gives way and permits the spindle fibers to pull them apart at the beginning of anaphase. As shown in Fig. 68, the centromere may be at or almost at one end (telocentric), near one end (acrocentric), near but not at the center (submetacentric), or at the center (metacentric). Since chromatids are shaped like rods they tend to bend where the centromere is attached as they are dragged through the vicid cytoplasm. They therefore may assume a variety of shapes during anaphase. They retain their rod-like appearance only if the attachment is at or very close to one end. If it is near, but not at, an end, they take a "J" shape, and if it is near the middle, a "U" shape.

The chromosomes of a single cell also vary considerably in size as well as shape. What determines the number of chromosomes in a cell is not known but their number and the assortment of sizes and shapes are the same for each individual of a species and for every cell in each individual except for the sex cells, which have half the number. In hu-

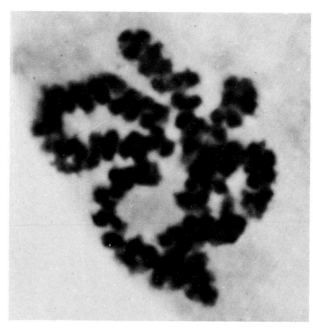

Fig. 67. *Chromosomes of Trillium erectum in meiotic division fixed so as to bring out the tendency to form helices. Whether or not chromosomes actually assume this form during life their tendency to do so when certain types of fixations are used, indicates a characteristic property of their substance.*

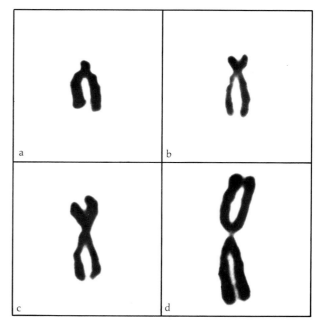

Fig. 68. *The four positions of the centromere or kinetochore. (a) telocentric; (b) acrocentric; (c) submetacentric; (d) metacentric.*

man somatic cells there are normally 46. It is customary to describe them as they appear at metaphase. Somatic chromosomes occur in pairs consisting of two homologues which are the replicas of the chromosomes received from each parent at the time of fertilization. In the sex cells there are only half as many chromosomes because the homologues have been separated by the meiotic divisions occurring in the gonads. The homologues from the two parents are randomly distributed between the two daughter cells during these divisions. The ability to recognize individual chromosomes or groups of chromosomes in somatic cells has made it possible for geneticists to correlate certain congenital anomalies with abnormalities in the chromosomes. A number of congenital syndromes in human beings have already been recognized as associated with specific chromosomal abnormalities such as mongolism.

These studies have been made possible by the development of techniques for growing blood cells or tissue cells in tissue culture, thereby providing

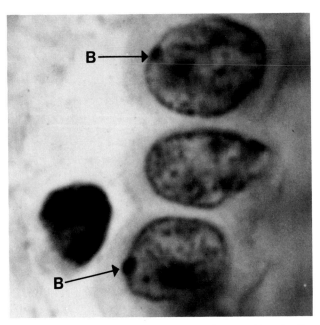

Fig. 70. *Cells from an ovarian tumor showing Barr bodies (B), one of the X chromosomes which remains condensed during interphase.*

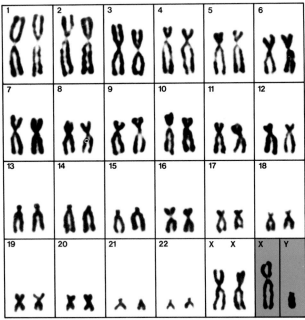

Fig. 69. *Karyotype of a normal woman. The blue area shows the X and Y chromosomes of a normal man whose karyotype would be the same as that for a woman except that a Y chromosome would be substituted for one of the X chromosomes.*

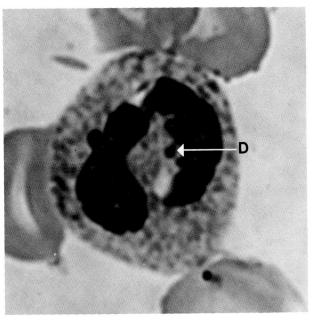

Fig. 71. *A polymorphonuclear leucocyte from a woman's blood showing a drumstick (D), the counterpart of the Barr body.*

78

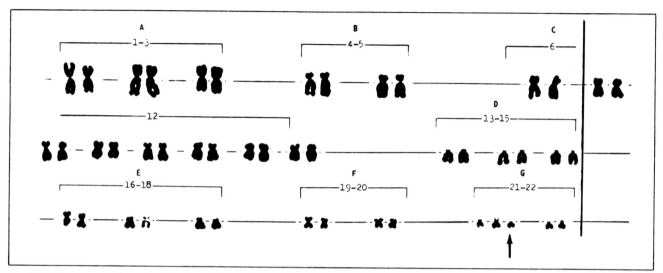

Fig. 72b. *Karyotype of a girl with Down's syndrome; there are three chromosomes instead of two in group 21, making a total of 47.*

a supply of rapidly dividing human cells. By the addition of colchicine to such a culture, mitosis is stopped at metaphase. The cells are then squashed and stained and the chromosomes examined. A suitable group is photographed and the individual chromosomes cut out and arranged in pairs according to size, i.e., a *karyotype* constructed (Fig. 69). Since mitosis is stopped in metaphase, the chromatids have not separated and the chromosomes are X-shaped.

As seen in the illustrations, the sex of an individual is revealed in his karyotype and this is often of practical importance, particularly in children with malformed or hermaphroditic genitalia. The sex of an individual can also be ascertained from tissue cells without resort to tissue culture. There is an observable chromatin mass at the periphery of the nucleus in somatic cells from women, which is not present in cells from men. This heterochromatin (known as a Barr body) is apparently one of the X chromosomes of the female which remains condensed during interphase. Thus, by observing the cells from the inner lining of the cheek or from a biopsy specimen for the presence of the Barr body (Fig. 70) or the polymorphonuclear leucocytes of a blood smear for "drum sticks" (Fig. 71), it is possible to tell whether the specimen

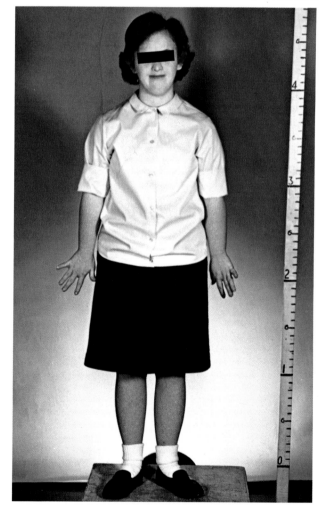

Fig. 72a. *A 16-year-old girl with Down's syndrome.*

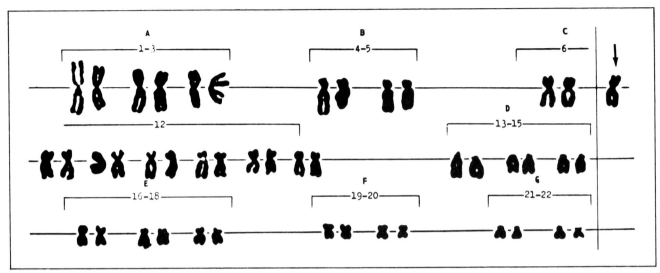

Fig. 73b. *Karyotype of a girl with Turner's syndrome. There is only one X chromosome, making a total of 45.*

is from a man or woman, a fact that may be of medicolegal as well as clinical importance.

Karyotypes have proven to be of great value in the study of human genetics. While the technique is time-consuming and laborious, it is a practical clinical tool. A continuingly growing number of congenital anomalies are being found to have characteristic karyotypes. These are helpful not only in understanding the etiology of the condition but have great prognostic value.

While this is not the place to discuss clinical syndromes, some examples of well known conditions resulting from chromosomal abnormalities seem called for. Three examples of abnormal karyotypes with photographs of typical patients with these chromosomal patterns are shown.

Downs syndrome or mongolism (Fig. 72) has puzzled clinicians for years because it occurs sporadically in families with no apparent hereditary stigmata. It is characterized by arrested mental and physical development with facial features that give the individual something of a mongolian appearance. It is often associated with other congenital defects, particularly congenital heart disease. These patients usually have three instead of two chromosomes in group 21, giving a total of 47.

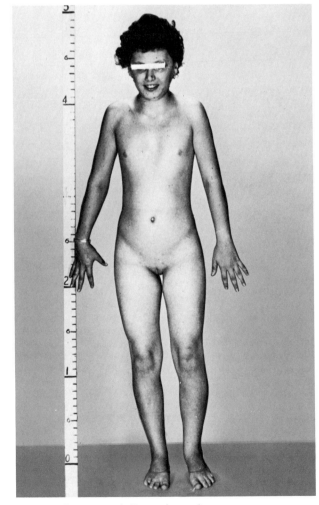

Fig. 73a. *Patient with Turner's syndrome.*

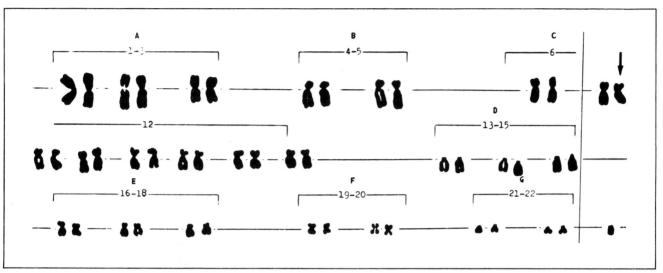

Patients with Turner's syndrome (Fig. 73) are usually short of stature and may be rather stocky and have a short or webbed neck and widely separated nipples. Otherwise they are normal appearing females. They do not, however, undergo puberty and develop normal primary and secondary sex characteristics. They usually have embryonic or "streak" gonads. They often have other abnormalities of which coarctation of the aorta is one of the most common. Some also have unexplained hypertension. Characteristically they have only one X chromosome making a total of 45. They consequently do not show the Barr body or drumstick. Hormone treatment will cause their secondary sex characteristics to develop and they can even be made to menstruate but they almost invariably remain sterile.

Kleinfelter's syndrome (Fig. 74) results in an individual with a male phenotype but as he develops his testes remain small and atrophic and he does not develop entirely normal secondary sex characteristics at puberty. They often have gynecomastia and may have a female body contour. The penis, scrotum and pubic hair may develop almost normally and the patients are usually capable of having an erection and ejaculating aspermic

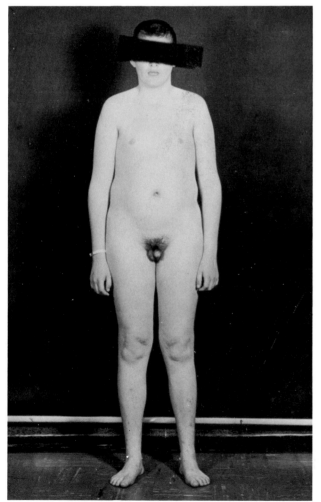

Fig. 74a. *A patient with Kleinfelters' syndrome.*

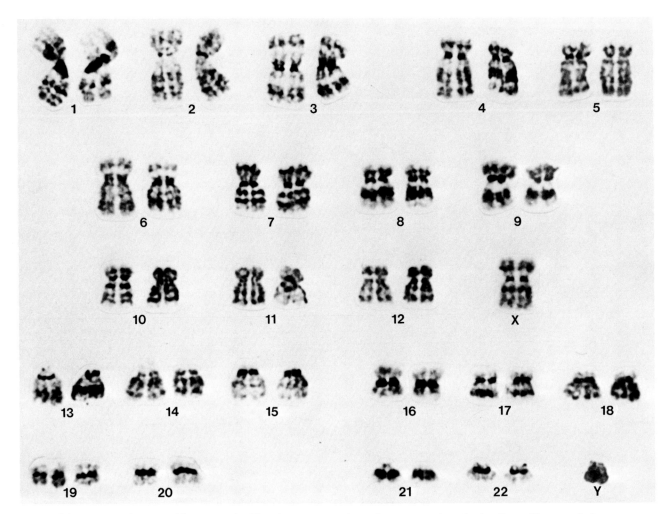

Fig. 75a. *A karyotype of a normal human male. The chromosomes have been stained with the Drets-Shaw technique.*

semen. But they are almost always sterile. As a rule these patients have two X chromosomes and one Y (Total 47). Consequently, they usually show a Barr body; its presence in an individual with a male phenotype strongly suggests this syndrome. These patients require encouragement more than treatment.

Generally there is good correlation between these clinical syndromes and the typical karyotypes shown but many minor variations occur.

Since assigning a chromosome to a particular group in the karyotype depends largely on the overall length of the chromosome and the position of the kinetochore, it is obvious that from time to time ambiguities will occur. Recently a new staining technique has been developed by Maximo E. Drets and Margery W. Shaw, which promises to give another valuable criterion for classification.

When this method of staining is used, bands are visualized in the chromosomes' arms. The bands are quite distinct in a well stained specimen and the patterns are constant and characteristic.

A typical karyotype stained by this new method is shown in Fig. 75a. The most reliable patterns for each pair of chromosomes is given diagrammatically in Fig. 75b.

The method has already been simplified so that

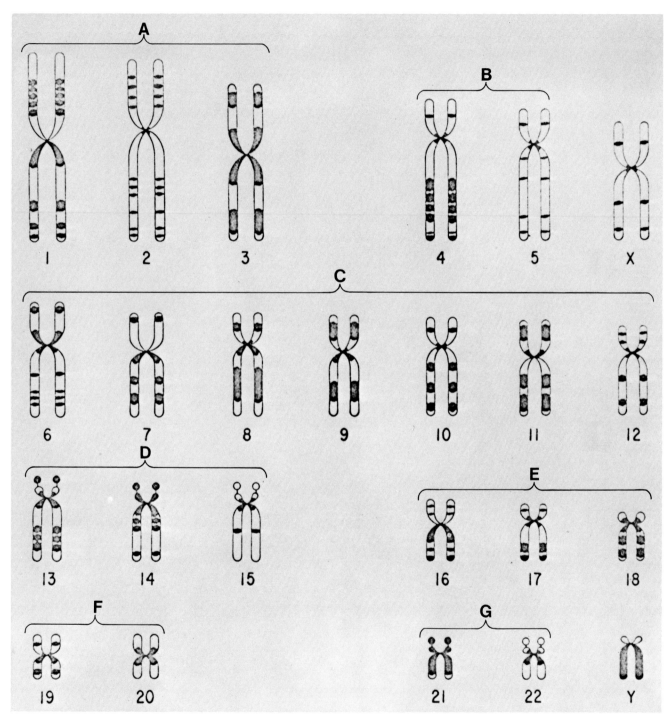

Fig. 75b. *A diagram of what have so far proved to be the most reliable patterns of bands for each chromosomal pair. (Within groups the numbering is arbitrary except for A_1, A_2, A_3, C_6, E_{16}, and Y).*

it is practical for diagnostic use although further research and experience will doubtless lead to improvements. The chromosomes are treated *in situ* with sodium hydroxide and then incubated with saline citrate solution and finally treated with Giemsa's stain.

GIANT CHROMOSOMES

Since the intimate details of the fine structure of most chromosomes are beyond the resolution of the light microscope and since the electron microscope has proved disappointing for revealing chromosomal details, much of our knowledge depends on the fortunate circumstances that in certain cells of certain species very large chromosomes occur—"giant" chromosomes whose details can be studied at moderate magnifications.

One of these chromosomes is the "lamp brush" chromosome (Figs. 76 and 77) found in the oocytes (developing female sex cells) of certain amphibians.

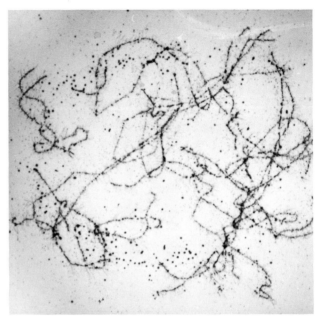

Fig. 76. *Chromosomes of Triturus oocyte as they appear under low power with the light microscope when the nucleus is squashed.*

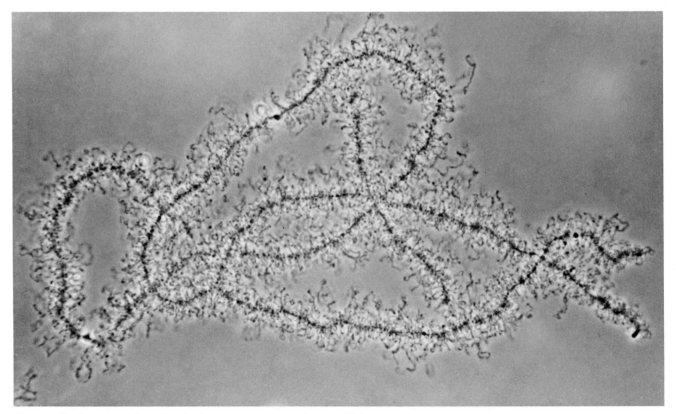

Fig. 77. *Single pair of lampbrush chromosomes from the newt Triturus—phase contrast microscopy.*

Fortunately, these chromosomes are large enough and refractile enough so that they can be examined unfixed and unstained with the phase contrast microscope. Consequently, their observed structure is that which they actually possess in life free from artifacts of preparation. Close examination reveals that they consist of a thin central strand from which the bristle-like projections arise (Fig. 78). The bristle-like projections are in actuality loops. The central strand seems to be thickened where the loops join it. These areas of thickening with their attached loops are called chromomeres.

Another type of giant chromosome (Figs. 79-82) is found in the salivary glands of certain insects (Diptera). These are quite different from the amphibian lamp brush chromosomes.

Although cylindrical, they look like ribbons across which are light and dark bands of varying widths (Fig. 82). The insects in which these giant chromosomes occur are small flies. They breed and de-

velop rapidly and are easily raised in the laboratory. They have consequently been extensively used for experiments in genetics. The circumstance of the same creature being suitable for genetic experiments and the study of chromosomal structure has proved to be most fortunate. While the chromosomes of most species are only visible during cell division, it has been shown that the giant chromosomes of insects and amphibians are actually interphase chromosomes. Thus, they make possible the observation of chromosomes in their normal functioning condition rather than in the much-contracted and metabolically inactive state which they assume during mitosis. In the case of the insects the chromosomes are few in number, easily differentiated from one another, and the pattern of the bands is constant. Consequently, specific regions within the chromosomes can be defined. It was not long, therefore, before geneticists realized the possibility of not only associat-

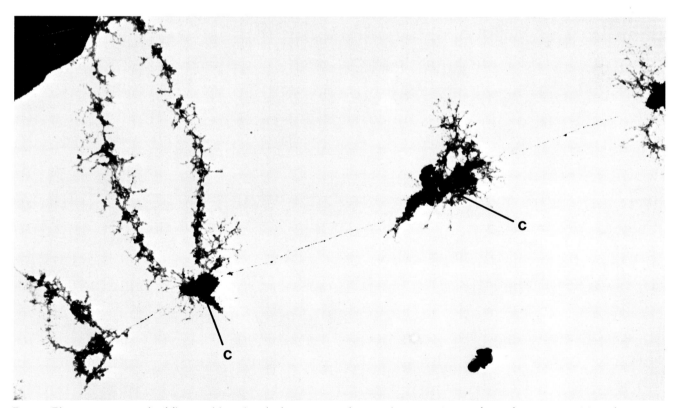

Fig. 78. *Electron micrograph of flattened lampbrush chromosome showing loops originating from chromomeres (c) and thin strands of DNA connecting chromomeres.*

ing certain genes with specific chromosomes but possibly determining their location within the individual chromosome. It proved possible to do this; and now after a great deal of painstaking work, the sites of many genes are known. It appears that each band is the locale of a gene or group of closely related genes. In this way, the gene, which was originally a purely conceptual idea of a unit of heredity has been given a physical embodiment.

Unexplained until recently, however, were certain swollen or puffed-up rings involving one or more bands. These rings had been observed in 1881 by E. G. Balbiani and are named after him, Balbiani rings (Figs. 80, 82 and 83).

Before going further into present concepts of the meaning of these puffs and the fine structure of chromosomes in general, it is necessary to consider the biochemistry of the nucleic acids.

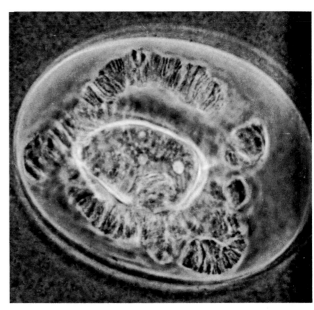

Fig. 79. *Giant chromosomes in the nucleus of a living salivary gland cell of Chironomus tentans showing a nucleolus —phase contrast.*

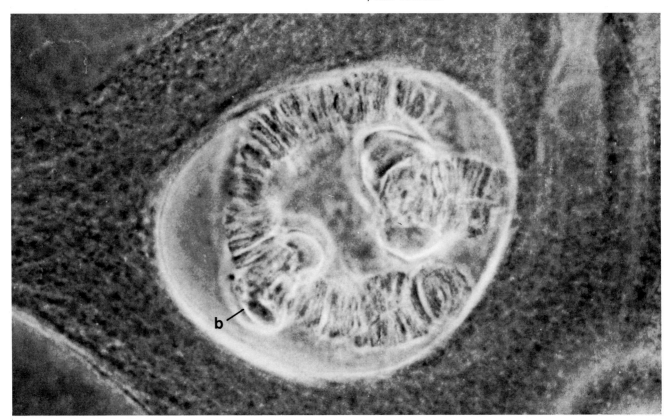

Fig. 80. *Giant chromosomes in the nucleus of a living salivary gland cell of Chironomus tentans showing a puff or Balbiani ring (b).*

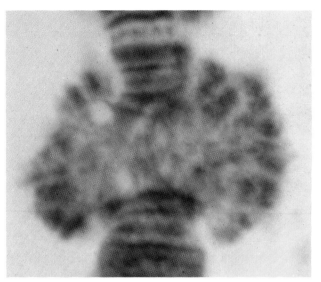

Fig. 83. *Part of chromosome IV of Chironomus tentans stained with light green. Bands show above and below the large puff. Its bluish-green color indicates the presence of protein.*

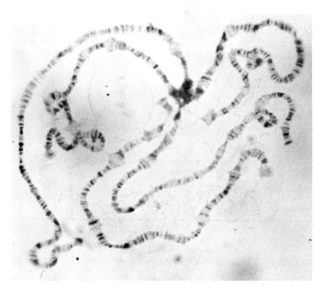

Fig. 81. *Chromosomes of Drosophilia virilis, stained to show the presence of histones.*

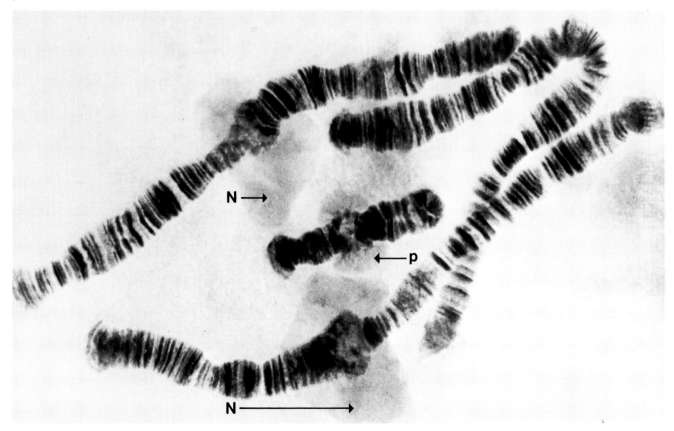

Fig. 82. *The four chromosomes of Chironomus tentans. The short chromosome has a large puff (p) and the two long chromosomes bear nucleoli (N).*

The Composition of Chromosomes

F. Meischer in 1868 separated out of cell nuclei, a substance which he called nuclein whose high content of phosphorus particularly interested him. Nuclein was found to consist of a complex acid subsequently called nucleic acid, combined with protein or protamine.

Following this discovery, the then new science of biochemistry concerned itself with the structure and metabolism of nucleic acids prepared from different tissues. It soon became clear that nucleic acid was composed of pyrimidines, purines, phosphoric acid and sugar, usually a pentose. The combination of a purine or pyrimidine, a sugar and phosphoric acid became known as a nucleotide; and nucleic acid was thought to consist of several nucleotides. At first it was thought there might be as few as four.

There are two varieties of nucleic acid whose most striking difference is their sugar molecule. The sugar in both forms of nucleic acid is the 5-carbon atom sugar, ribose. In the type found almost exclusively in the chromosomes this pentose lacks one oxygen atom that is present in the other. It is, therefore, known as desoxyribonucleic acid (DNA); the other type found in the nucleolus and scattered through the cytoplasm and in small amounts in the chromosomes is called ribonucleic acid (RNA). The nucleic acids are usually associated with proteins, both histones and proteins of higher order. Their chemical structure is illustrated in Fig. 84, which shows a short segment of RNA. This general scheme holds for DNA as well, with the pentose desoxyribose substituted for ribose.

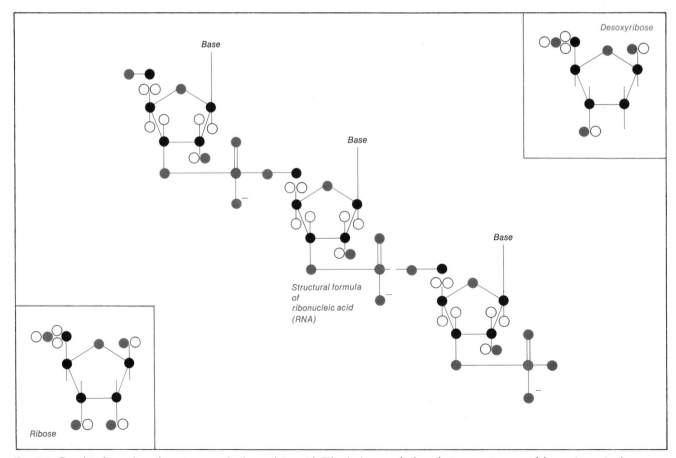

Fig. 84. *Graphic formulae of pentoses and ribonucleic acid. The linkages of phosphates, pentoses and bases in a single helix of DNA are similar.*

In the study of the chemistry of the nucleoproteins, various color-yielding reactions have been discovered that are characteristic for the acids and histones. They have been useful in locating the substances within cells. These color reactions can also be used for roughly estimating the amount of the substance stained in various parts of the cell.

Advances in genetics and cytology have led to the concept that the hereditary pattern of each individual is somehow coded in his chromosomes.

DESOXYRIBONUCLEIC ACID

This idea has been strengthened by the ability to associate specific genes with particular chromosomes and even with definite bands within the polytene chromosomes of insects.

The questions then arose as to which of the chemical constituents of chromosomes carries this code. Most of the early investigators of cell division believed that it was the nucleic acids discovered by F. Miescher.

However, Eduard Strasburger, who had originally believed this, later concluded that it was not the nucleic acids that carried the code because he and others observed that in some organisms at certain phases of cell development the nucleus no longer stained with the dyes specific for nucleic acid. They interpreted this to mean that at such times nucleic acid was absent. Since the hereditary pattern must have been carried through these stages when the nucleus would not stain, they concluded that something other than nucleic acid carried it. Their interpretation was wrong—the nucleic acid was there but stained lightly. Thus, for a long time most investigators believed that the hereditary code was carried by protein, although what protein was not determined. This idea persisted into the 1940's.

As a result of experiments with bacteria, it appeared that whatever the coding substance is, it is extractable. It can be demonstrated that an avirulent strain of bacteria can be transformed to a virulent strain by treating a growing culture of the avirulent strain with an extract of killed organisms of the virulent strain. Not all the avirulent organisms in the culture are so transformed, but some are, and these transmit this trait to their progeny. There were many attempts to discover the nature of the material that brought this transformation about.

In 1943, O. T. Avery, C. M. Macleod and M. McCarty announced that the material which caused the transformation of an R (rough) type of pneumococci to an S (smooth) type was desoxyribonucleic acid extracted from killed pneumococci of the S type. Their transforming material was destroyed by desoxyribonuclease which breaks down DNA but does not affect RNA or protein and it was not destroyed by ribonuclease that breaks down RNA or by proteolytic enzymes.

The work of A. E. Mirsky and Hans Ris about the same time also indicated DNA as the carrier of the hereditary code. They found that the amount

Key: ●*Oxygen* ●*Carbon* ○*Hydrogen* ●*Nitrogen*
●*Phosphorus*

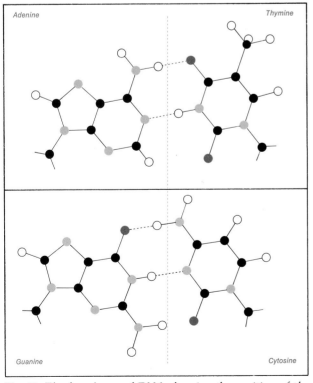

Fig. 85. *The four bases of DNA showing the position of the hydrogen bands.*

of DNA in all somatic cells of a given species was the same and that the sperm cells of the same species, which, of course, contained half the number of chromosomes, contained half the amount of DNA.

When it became clear that DNA codes the hereditary pattern, great interest arose in finding its molecular structure. It became obvious that DNA was a very large molecule that may contain thousands of nucleotides. How the nucleotides were arranged was, however, a matter of much conjecture and experiment.

There were important clues from chemical analysis of DNA. The molecule was made up of varying amounts of the four nucleotides of adenine, guanine, thymine and cytosine. While the amounts of these bases in the nucleic acids of different species varies, whatever the amounts of adenine, there is always an equivalent amount of thymine; and whatever the amount of guanine, there is an equivalent amount of cytosine. Furthermore, the pentose and phosphate moieties seemed to form long chains in which the two groups alternated. Physical studies indicated that the molecule is a long, thread-like one in which purines and pyrimidines are located at right angles to its axis. It was not, however, until M. H. F. Wilkins studied the X-ray diffraction of purified DNA (Fig. 87) and concluded that its structure was helical with cross-members more or less at right angles to the axis of the helix that James D. Watson and F. H. C. Crick hit upon their now-famous model of DNA (Fig. 86). While X-ray diffraction can suggest a type of structure, it cannot specifically locate atoms or groups of atoms. For more definitive information, it is necessary to set up a molecular model following the suggestions obtained from the diffraction patterns and check to see what sort of diffraction pattern the model would give. One then readjusts the model to give a diffraction pattern like that of the substance analyzed.

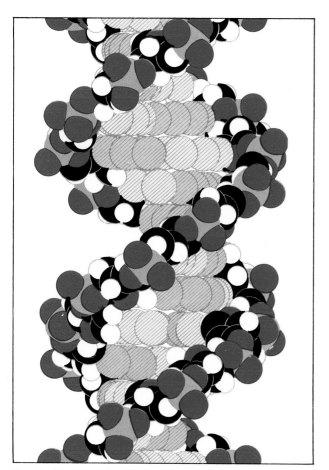

Fig. 86. *Model of the DNA molecule showing no space between atoms. The alternating phosphate and sugar moieties form the outer helixes, and pairs of bases the bridges.*

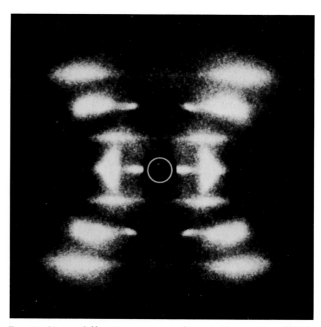

Fig. 87. *X-ray diffraction pattern of crystalline sodium DNA. The pattern of the bright spots indicates a helical structure.*

A key observation for Watson and Crick was that an adenine joined to a thymine has almost exactly the same length as a guanine joined to a cytosine. This made it possible that these combinations of a purine and a pyrimidine held together by hydrogen bonds were bridges connecting two long helices of alternate phosphate and pentose moieties (Fig. 86). These purine-pyrimidine bridges could be distributed in any order.

Not only was this model consistent with the experimental results, but it made possible many new conjectures that were confirmed by experiment. No concept in modern times has been more fruitful in opening up new fields for successful investigation. We are now not only finding out how genetic information is coded and passed from mother to daughter cell, but how this coded information controls life processes in all the cells of such complicated organisms as ourselves. For medicine, it has revealed a new realm where abnormalities can occur and where drugs can act, the DNA-RNA-protein synthesis system.

One of the first questions to be asked was, "How does so complicated a structure duplicate itself during cell division?" There is now excellent evidence that this is accomplished by a split which occurs between the purines and pyrimidines that allows the helices to separate. Each nucleotide of the single helical chains then acquires a new complementary nucleotide; each adenine is again united with a thymine and each guanine with a cytosine. Then the phosphate and pentose moie-

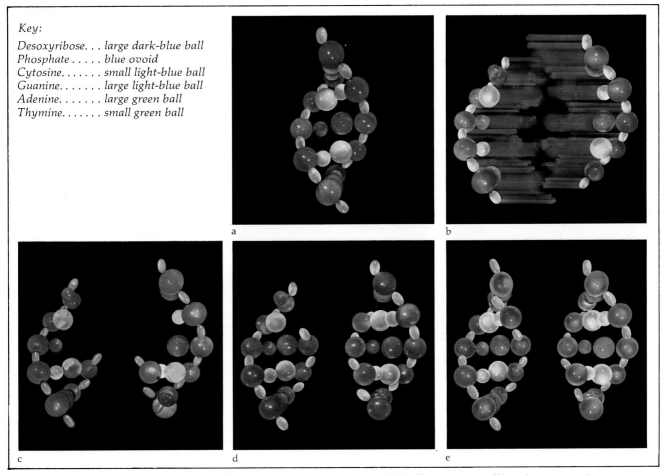

Key:

Desoxyribose. . . large dark-blue ball
Phosphate . . . . . blue ovoid
Cytosine. . . . . . . small light-blue ball
Guanine. . . . . . . large light-blue ball
Adenine. . . . . . . large green ball
Thymine. . . . . . . small green ball

a

b

c

d

e

Fig. 88. *The DNA molecule duplicates itself. From a resting state (a) the DNA fiber separates (b) and new complementary nucleotides move into place (c, d). Each of the two completed DNA fibers (e) contain one-half of the original fiber.*

ties of those newly acquired partners are united enzymatically and the process of duplication is complete (Fig. 88a-e).

Obviously, the coding must be accomplished by the arrangement of the four bases, adenine, guanine, thymine and cytosine. Mathematical analyses soon made it clear that the coding possibilities in a molecule as huge as DNA with thousands of bases are very great and entirely adequate.

A consideration of the biochemical aspects of the subject indicates that the coding problem is not so complex as might at first appear. The principal structural materials of cells are proteins or are made by enzymes which are proteins. Furthermore, the necessary energy to carry on all living processes is generated from food by reactions governed by enzymes. Consequently, most of the information that must be coded in the chromosomes consists of master patterns for all the proteins that make up the structure of the organism and regulate its metabolic processes. All of these proteins are composed of different arrangements of 20 amino acids. Consequently, the necessary coding would consist of a specific code word (to borrow a term from computer jargon) for each amino acid and then an arrangement of these code words in the proper order to make each of the necessary proteins. In addition, some sort of "punctuation" would be required to signal the beginning and end of each protein sequence.

This is an easily conceivable system, although the coding space required is staggering when the great size of many protein molecules is considered and also the vast number of different proteins in a complex organism. It has been determined that the code words for the amino acids consist of three nucleotides. With four bases (adenine, guanine, cytosine and thymine) 4^3 or 64 such words are possible, more than the number of amino acids. It was recently discovered that sometimes more than one code word may be used for the same amino acid.

RIBONUCLEIC ACID (RNA)

The form of nucleic acid (RNA) which is found in the nucleolus and the cytoplasm of the cell but to only a small extent within the chromosomes has a smaller molecule than DNA. Because the atoms composing RNA are not as symmetrically disposed as are those of DNA, physical methods such as X-ray diffraction have not proved so helpful for demonstrating the molecular form of RNA. In consequence, definitive knowledge of its structure has lagged behind that of DNA. It has a smaller molecular weight than DNA, contains uracil in place of thymine as one of its pyrimidine bases and ribose in place of desoxyribose. RNA does not have a regular double helical structure but is essentially single-stranded. Because DNA does not leave the nucleus, it was early conjectured that it is RNA that somehow transmits the information coded by DNA to the cytoplasm for use. This has proved to be true, but the process indeed has turned out to be a great deal more complicated than was thought at the beginning. One observation that has lent credence to the above idea is that electron micrographs almost invariably reveal openings or pores in the nuclear membrane (Fig. 63).

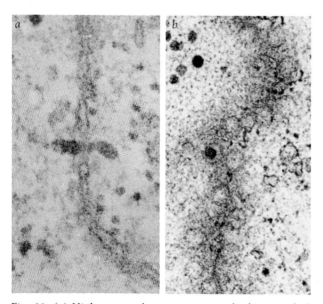

Fig. 89. *(a) High-power electron micrograph showing dark material, probably RNA, passing through an opening in the nuclear envelope. (b) Dark material in an oriface where section is tangential to the envelope (salivary gland of Chironomus).*

Certainly if it is to transfer information from the nucleus to the cytoplasm, RNA must be able to leave the nucleus, and furthermore, substances must be able to enter the nucleus to start and stop RNA production. These openings would be logical pathways for such traffic. Recently, graphic demonstration of such a passage of material has been obtained (Fig. 89). Evidence indicates that most of the RNA found in the cytoplasm is formed in the nucleus using DNA as a template (primer) for its formation.

The formation of RNA is the principal function of the nucleus in the resting cell. The synthesis of RNA is, in general, similar to the duplication of DNA. The double helix of the DNA splits apart as in DNA duplication, but only a limited length of the DNA fiber is involved—that part that carries the code for the particular kind of RNA that is about to be formed (Figs. 90a and b). But instead of both halves of the strand acting as templates, only one does (Figs. 90c and d). This one strand then attracts complementary nucleotides which contain ribose instead of desoxyribose and uracil in place of thymine, the nucleotides are joined to-

Key: Desoxyribose. . . large dark-blue ball
Ribose. . . . . large red ball
Phosphate. . . . . . blue ovoid
Cytosine. . . . . . . small light-blue ball
Guanine. . . . . . . large light-blue ball
Adenine. . . . . . . large green ball
Thymine. . . . . . . small green ball
Uracil. . . . . small red ball

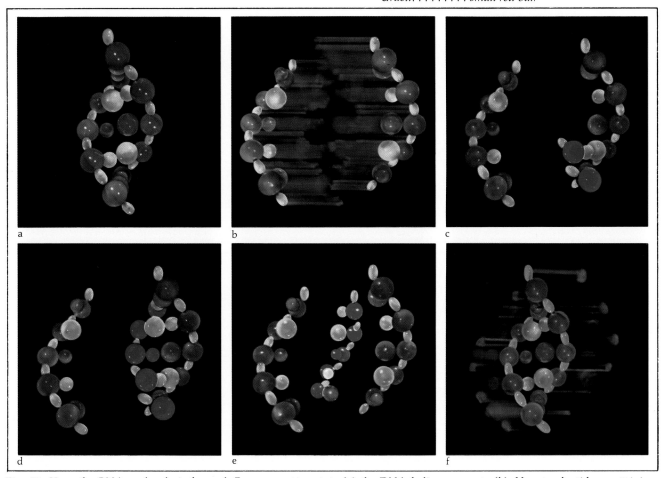

Fig. 90. *How the RNA molecule is formed. From a resting state (a) the DNA helixes separate (b). New nucleotides containing ribose instead of desoxyribose move into place on right-hand fiber (c). As the RNA fiber is completed (d), it moves away (e) and the separated DNA helixes rejoin (f).*

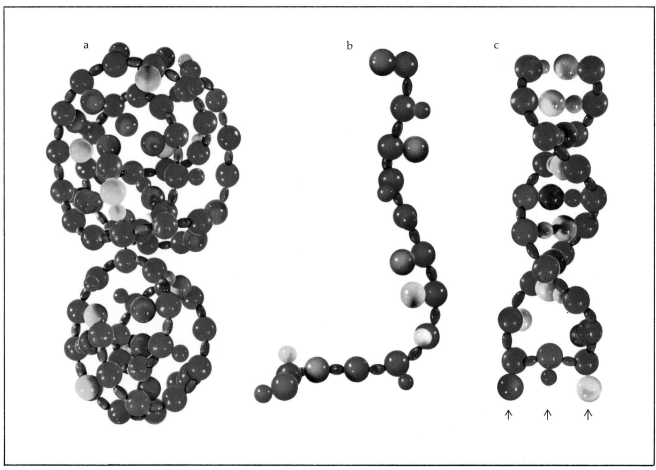

Fig. 91. *Models a , b & c of the three types of RNA.*
  a: The two coiled molecules of Ribosomal RNA
  b: Messenger-RNA
  c: Transfer-RNA
  d: Diagram of the cloverleaf configuration for transfer
    RNA.

gether by a specific enzyme and a single-stranded nucleic acid is formed which is freed from the DNA template and is ready to migrate out of the nucleus (Fig. 90e).

It has been discovered that there are three types of RNA, each with a different molecular size and configuration.

Ribosomal RNA
RNA is the main constituent of the ribosomes that line the endoplasmic reticulum and that are found free in the cytoplasm. They are composed of two

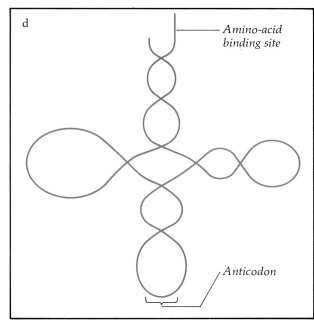

Amino-acid binding site

Anticodon

molecules of RNA, the larger about twice the size of the smaller, which are closely associated when functioning. The molecules are thought to be sort of wound up into balls by complementary groups of purine and pyrimidine adhering by hydrogen bonds wherever they come into contact (Fig. 91a). Ribosomal RNA and the RNA in the nucleolus are very similar. Probably the nucleolus is a reservoir of ribosomal RNA and the site of its formation. Ribosomes also contain protein which may help maintain their compact structure. The ribosome is composed of two associated molecules of RNA and is always the locale of protein synthesis, but how it participates in the process is not known.

Transfer RNA

Transfer RNA is the smallest of the three types. It may coil about itself like a twisted hairpin and thus have a double helical structure over part of its length in which complementary bases are joined together. It, however, always contains a loop (Fig. 91c, arrows) in which there are three free bases whose arrangement is specific for one of the 20 amino acids called an anticodon, which fits into a place on a messenger RNA that calls for this particular amino acid. Of the two free ends of the transfer RNA hairpin, one contains a free guanine, the other two cytosines and an adenine in that order. It is to the latter that the amino acid is attached. This is the simplest representation that is consistent with most of the experimental data. A cloverleaf configuration (Fig. 91d) probably more nearly represents the facts but even this may be too simple. Transfer RNA binds itself to a specific amino acid and carries it to the ribosomal site of protein synthesis. Here its three base code on the loop finds its proper place on the messenger RNA, and its amino acid is attached to the growing polypeptide chain of the forming protein. Protein synthesis will be discussed in more detail later.

Messenger RNA

Messenger RNA is of smaller molecular weight than the ribosomal RNA and is not wound and twisted upon itself as the former is. It appears to be a single-strand of nucleotides (Fig. 91b) united by their pentose and phosphate groups. This is the form that actually transports the coded information for protein synthesis out of the nucleus. It makes temporary contact with ribosomes and passes through or around them, and before it has emerged from one ribosome may make contact with one or more others.

Correlation of Molecular with Microscopic Structure

If the DNA molecule is a long helical fiber, how are such fibers arranged in the chromosomes? The simplest chromosomes, such as those of viruses, bacteria and blue-green algae, probably consist of a single fiber in the form of a loop, as shown in Fig. 92. As has been seen, Fig. 24, the DNA of mitochondria is of this primative form. In the living organism, however, this loop is much folded and twisted but its DNA is not combined with histone. It has therefore been suggested by Hans Ris that these simple structures not be called chromosomes but genophores. This is a logical distinction because in these simple organisms there are no well defined units that resemble chromosomes of the higher forms and there is no nuclear membrane. In true chromosomes there are probably two or more strands of DNA in combination with histone.

As indicated earlier, the giant lampbrush and polytene chromosomes have proved to be very useful research material. It is therefore, necessary to understand their structure in order to comprehend how research with them relates to higher forms.

LAMP BRUSH CHROMOSOMES

The giant lampbrush chromosomes occur in the oocytes of newts during early prophase of the first meiotic division. At this time a great deal of material, yolk and other substances, are being synthesized and the cells have become large. The

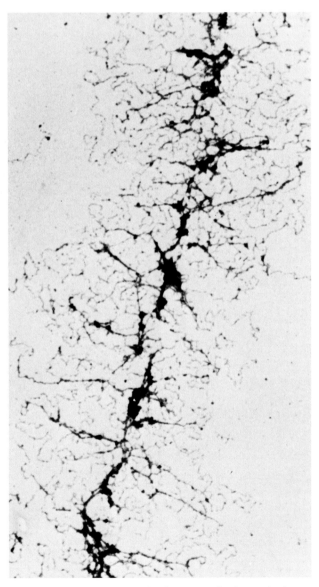

Fig. 93. *Electron micrograph of a piece of a loop of a lampbrush chromosome. The axis of the loop is DNA but the fine fibrils extending from it are RNA.*

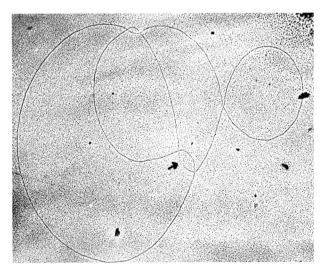

Fig. 92. *Electron micrograph (X 15,000) of loop-shaped DNA molecule from Lambda phage. The DNA was extracted, combined with cytochrome C and spread in a monolayer on water.*

chromosomes are, therefore, presumably producing the large amounts of RNA needed for the synthesis of these materials. Also, at this time each pair of homologous chromosomes have become associated and are attached at one or more chiasma. Such a pair is seen in Fig. 77 and at the moderate magnification of this phase-contrast photomicrograph, a good deal of their structure can be made out. They appear to consist of a long central cord from which bristle-like projections radiate. An important observation is that if the chromosome is stretched by applying tension to its ends, some of the bristles disappear. In other words, the bristles are actually loops continuous with the central strand and not structures attached to it. Their loop-like structure is also revealed in electron micrographs. (Fig. 78)

The electron microscope also reveals thread-like material extending from the fiber forming the loop, i.e., bristles on the bristle (Fig. 93). This

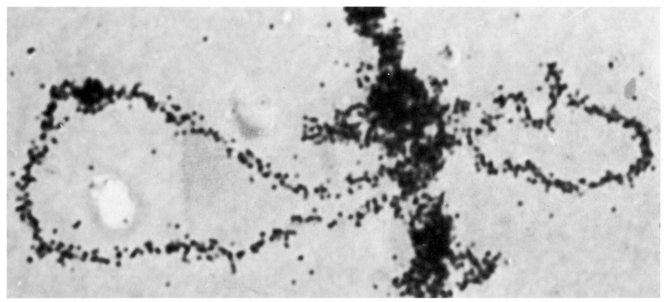

Fig. 94. *Autoradiograph of a pair of loops of a lampbrush chromosome of Triturus treated with radioactive uridine. The numerous black dots indicate a high concentration of radioactivity in the loops.*

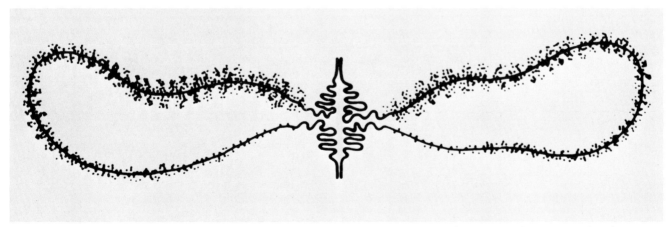

Fig. 95. *Probable structure of a lampbrush chromosome. The loops extending from the chromomeres (c) are DNA but the fibrils extending from the loop are RNA.*

fringe has been shown to be RNA since it is removed leaving only the loop, when the chromosomes are treated with ribonuclease which specifically attacks RNA. Desoxyribonuclease, on the other hand, fragments the loop and the main strand of the chromosome.

That there are considerable quantities of newly formed RNA associated with the loops is confirmed by autoradiograms (Fig. 94) made on the chromosomes of animals who have been given radioactive uridine, the nucleotide containing uricil which, as mentioned previously, is a pyrimidine found only in RNA.

These and other findings are consistent with a structure for the lampbrush chromosomes diagrammed in Fig. 95. The main strand or backbone of the chromosome consists of two double helixes of DNA which at intervals along their length become very much twisted to form knotlike enlargements from each of which a single loop extends laterally. Between these twisted-up regions called chromomeres, the two filaments of DNA are smooth and untwisted. The RNA is largely in the fringe of fibrils eminating from the loops. The loop would, therefore, appear to be the part of the DNA fiber that is at the moment active. Untwisting into a loop seems a nesessary preliminary to the production of RNA. When they are no longer needed for RNA production the loops are apparently drawn in by regaining their twists. It is thought that there are only two strands of DNA in each lampbrush chromosome, one strand for each chromatid, as indicated in the diagram (Fig. 95).

POLYLENE CHROMOSOMES

The fine structure of the insect giant chromosomes is somewhat more difficult to reveal, largely because of the compact nature of these huge chromosomes which are easily seen at low magnifications in living tissue (Figs. 79 and 80). They occur only in certain cells of developing insects, notably the salivary glands of fruit flies and midges.

Polytene chromosomes have been shown to con-

tain many multiples of the normal amount of DNA, indicating that the original strands of DNA have replicated many times without the cell dividing. In a single chromosome there may be 1024 strands or even four times this number in some species according to Hewson Swift. This amounts to ten replications, $(2)^{10} = 1024$.

These strands remain together and lined up in phase, i.e., the fibers after replication have not shifted longitudinally and the individual genes are accurately aligned across the bundle. It is this that gives rise to the cross banding. Each of these chromosomes (Fig. 82) must contain two chromatids and both presumably have participated in the numerous replications, but they are usually not distinguishable.

The DNA is largely concentrated in the dark bands and there is very little in the intervening light ones. If these chromosomes are composed of many parallel fibers the increased concentration of DNA in the dark bands could be explained if those were areas where the strands were much twisted and folded. Consequently, a model such as Fig. 96 would indicate the structure of those chromosomes. The conspicuous puffs, Balbiani

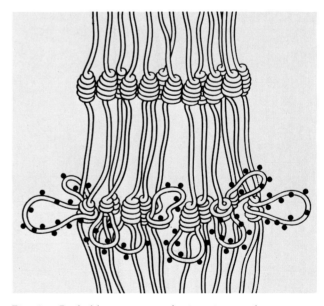

Fig. 96. *Probable structure of giant insect chromosome. Areas of twisting represent dense bands. The uncoiling lower band is the beginning of a puff. The black dots are RNA.*

rings, which occur (Figs. 82 and 83) could then be bands, i.e., genes, which have untwisted and expanded to permit RNA formation. In confirmation of this it has been possible to demonstrate large concentrations of newly formed RNA in these puffs by the use of radio-active uridine (Fig. 98). Electron micrographs of puffs show them to be composed of fine fibrils among which are many globular granules (Figs. 97a and b). The fibrils are interpreted as the DNA fibrils and the granules as RNA. A graphic demonstration of the structure is seen in Fig. 97c, whose orientation in the puff has been indicated by insetting into Fig. 97a. Here the RNA has been enzymatically

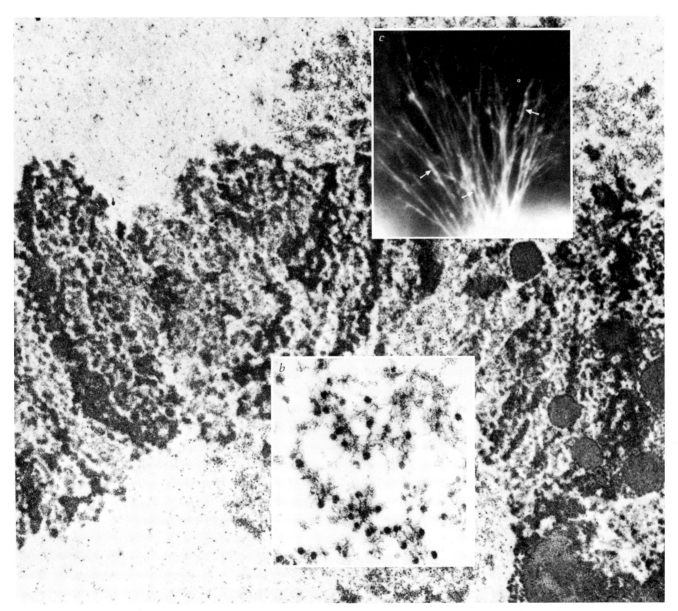

Fig. 97. *An electron micrograph of a longitudinal section of a Balbiani ring shows a network of DNA fibrils and many RNA granules (a). Section of puff at higher power (b). The DNA framework of the puff has been revealed (c), by dissolving away the RNA with ribonuclease and staining the remaining DNA with acridine orange and taking a fluorescence micrograph. The thick bundles at the base of the puff subdivide into smaller ones toward the periphery. Approximate orientation, only, is shown.*

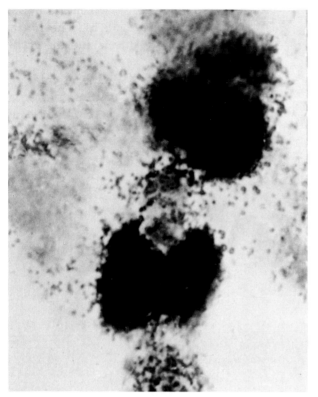

Fig. 98. *Autoradiograph of chromosome IV of Chironomus tentans which had been treated with radioactive uridine. The concentration of radioactivity in the puffs indicates large amounts of newly formed RNA.*

removed and the DNA specifically stained; in this way the DNA framework of the structure is revealed.

Ulrich Clever has correlated the expansion of two particular bands into puffs with the beginning of the molt which transforms the larva to a pupa in one of these insects. Furthermore, he has been able to stimulate the appearance of these puffs with all the accompanying events by the administration of a specific hormone, ecdysone. The chromosomal puff is of great importance because it is an easily observable signal of gene activity.

VERTIBRATE CHROMOSOMES

The work of Hans Ris on the erythrocyte nuclei of Triturus viridescens gives further evidence of how DNA fibers are packed in the nuclei of vertebrates. When material from these nulei is spread

in a monolayer on water a network of 250A threads is seen (Fig. 99a). By brief treatment with sodium citrate these are seen to be made up of two 100A fibers twisted together (Fig. 99b). Branches result from one of these fibers looping out and twisting on itself. Longer treatment with sodium citrate results in completely separating the 100A fibers which have many knot-like bumps, suggesting that some twisting is still present (Fig. 99c). Treatment with pronase removes the histone and yields fibers of 25A that are only twisted here and there

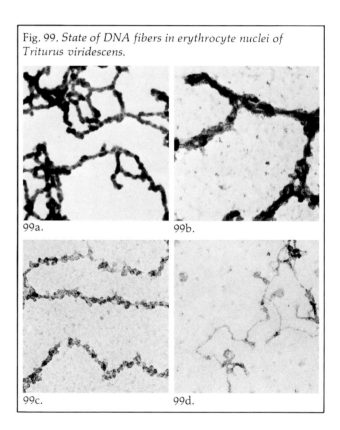

Fig. 99. *State of DNA fibers in erythrocyte nuclei of Triturus viridescens.*

99a. 99b.

99c. 99d.

Fig. 99a. *Network of 250 Angstrom fibers resulting from spreading the nucleohistone on water.*

Fig. 99b. *Structure of 250 Angstrom fibers revealed by 10-second treatment with 5 mM sodium citrate.*

Fig. 99c. *Rough 100 Angstrom fibers separated by longer treatment with 5 mM sodium citrate.*

Fig. 99d. *The 100 Angstrom fibers further unwound to single 25 Angstrom DNA fibers by digesting with promase to remove histone.*

and are probably DNA double helixes (Fig. 99d). The histones are probably responsible for the primary twisting and folding of DNA and bivalent ions for secondary twisting and folding.

That human chromosomes are also composed of primarily and secondarily twisted and folded strands of DNA is brought out in the work of E. J. DuPraw, G. F. Bahr, and A. M. Golomb who have studied the properties of the DNA in human chromosomes using both transmission and scanning electron microscopy. An acrocentric human chromosome is shown in Fig. 100a as revealed by transmission electronmicrography. Its wooly nature is obvious and lumpy strands of twisted DNA can be seen extending from it in all directions. While the resolving power of the scanning electronmicroscope is less than that of the transmis-

sion instrument it gives a graphic view of the surface contour. A scanning electronmicrograph of another acrocentric human chromosome is shown in Fig. 100b. One of the two long limbs extends upward and the other to the upper right and is partially cropped. One of the short arms extends to the left and the other almost directly at the reader.

In this micrograph the fibers appear somewhat larger than they actually are because they have been given a gold-palladium coating 150A thick. This "shadowing" is responsible for the three dimensional quality of the image.

It is interesting that a strand of DNA connects the two long arms of the chromosome.

Fig. 100b. *Scanning electron micrograph of an acrocentric human chromosome. One of the two long limbs extends upward and the other to the upper right and is partially cropped. One of the short arms extends to the left and the other almost directly at the reader.*

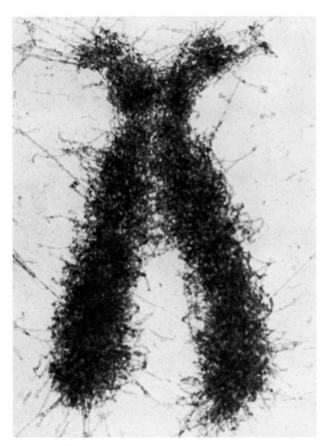

Fig. 100a. *Transmission electron micrograph of an acrocentric human chromosome. It is composed of a mass of knotty strands.*

Genes in Action

A graphic demonstration of RNA transcription is found in the recent work of O. L. Miller, Barbara R. Beatty, Barbara A. H. Hamkalo and C. A. Thomas at the Oak Ridge National Laboratories. It concerns ribosomal RNA production in nucleoli of the oocytes of Triturus viridescens. (These are the same cells in whose nuclei the giant lampbrush chromosomes are found.) In these large nuclei many (several hundred) extrachromosomal nucleoli are found in which active RNA production is taking place. These nucleoli consist of a peripheral zone made up of granules which are largely RNA and a central fibrous core that contains both DNA and RNA.

If some of these nucleoli are separated out, ruptured and some of their contents spread on a grid and prepared for electron microscopy, interesting structures are revealed (Fig. 101). One sees long,

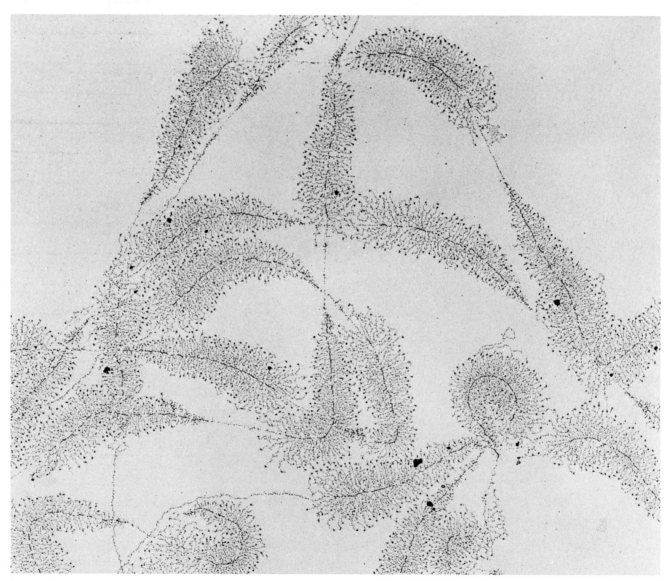

Fig. 101. *Electron micrograph (x25,000) of material from the nucleolar core from an oocyte of Triturus veridescens showing RNA fibrils radiating from a DNA core. Genes are producing rRNA. Each pine-tree-like grouping of RNA fibrils indicates the local of a codon for an rRNA molecule.*

thin fibers along whose length at rather regular intervals are pine tree-like accumulations of fine fibers, more or less at right angles to the central fiber. At the top of the pine tree the fibers are very short and they increase in length until a maximum is reached; then for an interval there are no fibers. This pattern is repeated at quite regular intervals along the fibers.

By the use of the specific enzymes, desoxyribonuclease and ribonuclease, and other means, it was found that the central fiber is DNA and the branch-like fibers are RNA.

The author's interpretation of this micrograph is that the long DNA fibers contain genes for one or both of the RNA molecules that make up the ribosomes and that the production of these was actually taking place at the time of fixation. Many of these molecules are being produced simultaneously. The long branches of the pine tree are those most nearly completed and the short branches are those whose transcription has just begun. We see all stages of the process.

At a higher magnification (Fig. 102), a roughly spherical nodule can be seen where each branch joins the trunk. This is interpreted to be the RNA polymerase molecule in the act of joining the nucleotides together; its size is that which this enzyme should have.

When this clear-cut picture of RNA production was observed in the nucleoli of the same nucleus in which the giant lampbrush chromosomes are found, the question naturally arises: "Are the lampbrush chromosomes producing other forms of RNA by a similar process?" The loops that form the bristles of the lampbrush are presumably DNA unwound for the purpose of producing RNA. Investigation revealed that this was the case. But difficulties were encountered, because here much larger molecules were being produced. Whereas in the nucleoli the genes being transcribed were small enough so that many could be placed in the field of the electron microscope, in the chromosomes themselves much larger genes were being transcribed and the field of the electron microscope could encompass only part of one, at the

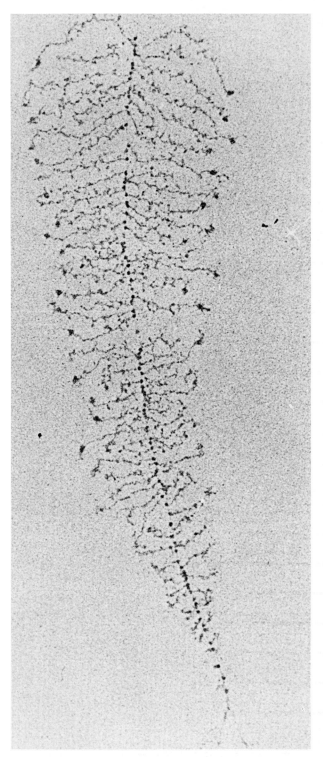

Fig. 102. *Higher magnification of the same material as in Figure 101. A small spherical mass of what is presumably RNA polymerase can be seen at the base of each RNA fibril.*

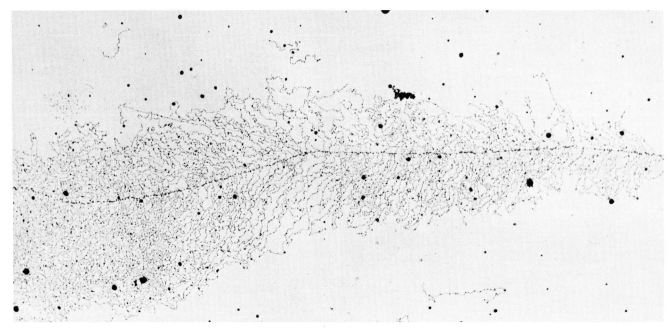

Fig. 103. *Electron micrograph (X 29,000) of a piece of a loop of a lampbrush chromosome of Triturus veridescens showing RNA fibrils radiating from a DNA core. Presumed RNA polymerase molecules are also visible.*

magnification that was required. That a process similar to that seen in the nucleoli was going on, however, can be seen in Fig. 103.

THE SYNTHESIS OF PROTEIN

The site of protein synthesis is the ribosome which is usually located on the outer surface of the endoplasmic reticulum. The two parts of the ribosomes are closely held together so that in electron micrography they appear as a single unit. The ribosome, however, remains inactive until a molecule of messenger RNA (mRNA) makes contact with it (Fig. 104a). The messenger RNA attaches to the smaller of the two parts and passes through, alongside, or around it. When this occurs, amino acids attached to molecules of their specific transfer RNA (sRNA) are attracted and temporarily attached to the larger part of the ribosome (Fig. 104b). Each molecule of transfer RNA, once it has fitted itself into the proper place on the messenger RNA, leaves its amino acid attached to the ribosome and goes free (Fig. 104c). The amino acids

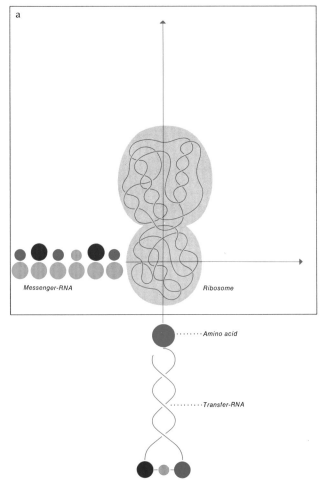

a

Messenger-RNA · · · · · · · · · Ribosome

· · · · · · · · Amino acid

· · · · · · · · Transfer-RNA

then become fused together, one after the other, in the order ordained by the messenger RNA until the protein chain is completed (Figs. 104d, e and f). There is a specific type of transfer RNA for each amino acid and the amino acid must be attached to it by a specific enzyme. The transfer RNA seems necessary to fit the amino acid into its proper place, because it is the transfer RNA rather than the amino acid itself that fits into the messenger RNA template. An enzyme effects the union of the positioned amino acids while still attached to the larger rRNA molecule.

It has been demonstrated that a single strand of messenger RNA may code the synthesis of more than one protein, usually functionally related proteins. This means that as it passes through the ribosome it must somehow effect the release of one protein chain before starting the next. How this is accomplished is not known, but whatever its mechanism it must be coded in the mRNA and in the DNA which served as the pattern.

It is interesting that one, and only one, messenger RNA can make a specific protein or group of proteins and that a specific transfer RNA is required for each amino acid, but that the ribosome has no specificity. It can be used by one messenger RNA to make one protein and as soon as released be used by another messenger RNA to make a different protein.

The useful life of the molecules of mRNA is limited; frequent replacements are necessary. This is why the presence of the nucleus is essential for the cell's continued existence. Obviously, any factor that influences the formation of any form of RNA or its functioning will correspondingly influence the functioning of the cell.

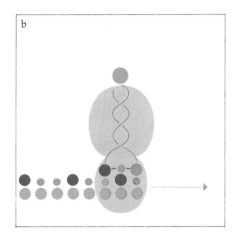

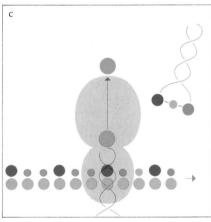

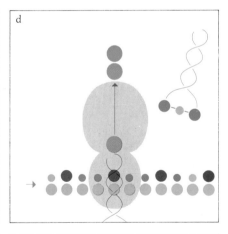

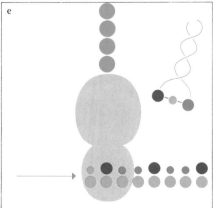

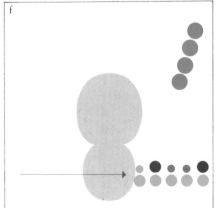

Fig. 104. *The synthesis of protein.*

Key: *Cytosine* . . . . . *small light-blue ball*
   Guanine . . . . . *large light-blue ball*
   Adenine . . . . . *large green ball*
   Thymine . . . . . *small green ball*
   Uracil . . . . *small red ball*

POLYRIBOSOMES

It has been known for some time that the ribosomes are usually arranged on the surface of the endoplasmic reticulum in simple patterns. The reason was at first not clear. Now, however, it is believed that ribosomes normally function in groups and that when the groups become disorganized their function ceases. It is not known what is responsible for the patterned grouping of the ribosomes—whether it is a property of the ribosomes themselves or something in the surface of the endoplasmic reticulum or some other factor.

An attractive theory is that it may be the messenger RNA that is responsible.

As soon as the forward end of messenger RNA is free of one ribosome (Figs. 105a-d), it is ready to contact another. Thus it may thread itself through several, causing protein synthesis to take place in each, the process in the one first contacted being a step or two ahead of that in the second, and the second correspondingly ahead of the third, and so on. In this way several ribosomes are temporarily held together in a group by the messenger RNA. In a given cell actively producing a given protein, these groups have a certain uniformity as to number of ribosomes and arrangement. Such groups are called "polyribosomes" or "polysomes" (Fig. 106). Under favorable circumstances the electron microscope may show a fine fibril connecting such a group of ribosomes. Presumably the connecting strand is messenger RNA.

Recently, Russell Ross and Earl P. Bendit have made both biochemical and careful electronmicrographical studies of the fibroblasts of scorbutic animals. Normal fibroblasts actively producing collagen have a rich endoplasmic reticulum whose surface is covered with many ribosomes. Furthermore, most of these ribosomes are normally arranged into double rows and loose spiral patterns. On the other hand, in the fibroblasts of scorbutic animals that are incapable of producing mature collagen, the ribosomes are randomly distributed

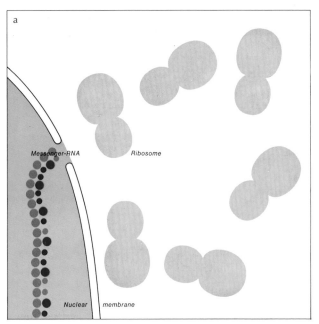

Fig. 105. *Polyribosomes.*

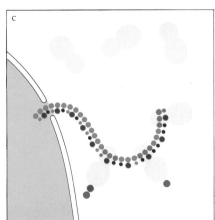

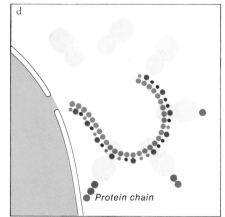

and no pattern is discernible. With the administration of ascorbic acid, the normal pattern of ribosomal arrangement returns promptly and so does the production of mature collagen. What causes the breaking up of the ribosomal patterns remains to be discovered. Interference with messenger RNA formation is one of the possibilities (Fig. 107).

After seeing diagramatically how the ribonucleic acids function in the synthesis of protein it is interesting to return once more to the reality of an experiment involving the prokaryotic chromosome of a strain of Escherichia coli.

This strain is very sensitive to osmotic changes and is easily lysed with distilled water. When so ruptured much of the nuclear material is extruded. The electron microscope reveals that this material consists of fine fibers to which strings of granules are attached at irregular intervals. The fibers are dissolved by DNAase but not RNAase. The latter removes the strings of granules from the fibers which it leaves untouched. The granules have the size and configuration of E. coli ribosomes.

A fiber with attached strings of granules is shown in Fig. 108. The part of the DNA fiber to which the strings of granules are attached is probably a gene which at the time of fixation was being transcribed to produce a molecule of messenger RNA. The mRNA fiber is not visible because it has been covered with ribosomes as fast as it was formed. (The ribosomes had already been formed on another DNA fiber.) The strings of granules are therefore polyribosomes still attached to the DNA fiber by a mRNA fiber whose transcription is not yet complete.

The ribosomes are probably already translating the code on the mRNA and producing protein molecules. There is biochemical confirmation that transcription, translation and protein synthesis take place in rapid succession in bacteria. For example, almost all the mRNA in E. coli is closely associated with rRNA.

ANTIBIOTIC ACTION

A number of antibiotics are already known to act on the DNA-RNA-Protein synthesis system.

Fig. 106. *Polyribosomes of yeast (X 150,000) from a sucrose suspension. The thin strands connecting the ribosomes may be Messenger-RNA. Ribosomes in intact cells may have a more regular arrangement than shown here.*

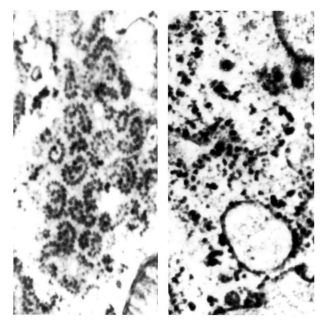

Fig. 107. *Polyribosomes in spiral patterns on the endoplasmic reticulum of a normal guinea pig fibroblast (left). In a scorbutic animal (right) the patterns are lost.*

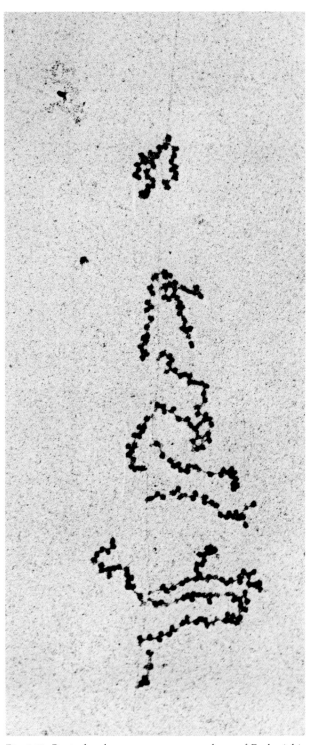

Fig. 108. *Part of a chromosome or genophore of Escherichia coli showing attached polyribosomes. Ribosomes have attached themselves to forming strands of mRNA so closely that the strands themselves are not visible.*

For example, actinomycin has been found to specifically inhibit messenger RNA transcription. Its action is so complete, in adequate doses, and so specific that it has become an important research tool for ascertaining the effect of stopping RNA synthesis without interfering otherwise with protein synthesis.

Another antibiotic, puromycin, stops protein synthesis but does not interfere with RNA formation. It also has become a useful research tool. Recently observations have shown that cyclohexamid also specifically inhibits protein synthesis while permitting RNA formation.

The new antibiotic, lincomycin, also inhibits protein synthesis in bacteria, apparently by preventing the temporary attachment of the transfer RNA to the ribosome. All these antibiotics may have other actions than their effect on protein synthesis.

A particularly interesting example of antibiotic action is the effect of streptomycin in streptomycin-sensitive microorganisms (Figs. 109a-e). In the presence of the antibiotic normal messenger RNA and normal transfer RNA are produced. However, the protein manufactured is useless because the code on the messenger RNA is misread and wrong amino acids are inserted in the protein chain with sufficient frequency to make the protein useless to the organism. The mechanism by which these mistakes are produced could be by interfering with the action of one or more of the enzymes that attach the amino acids to the specific transfer RNAs. There seems to be more evidence, however, that the trouble is in the ribosome, since it appears as if it is the action of the antibiotic specifically on the ribosomes rather than the other components of the system that causes the misreading.

Such evidence as there is at present seems to indicate that it is one of the protein components of the ribosome that is in some way acted on by the antibiotic.

While the antibiotic causes useless protein to be made in a normal organism, a mutant which would ordinarily not survive because its DNA

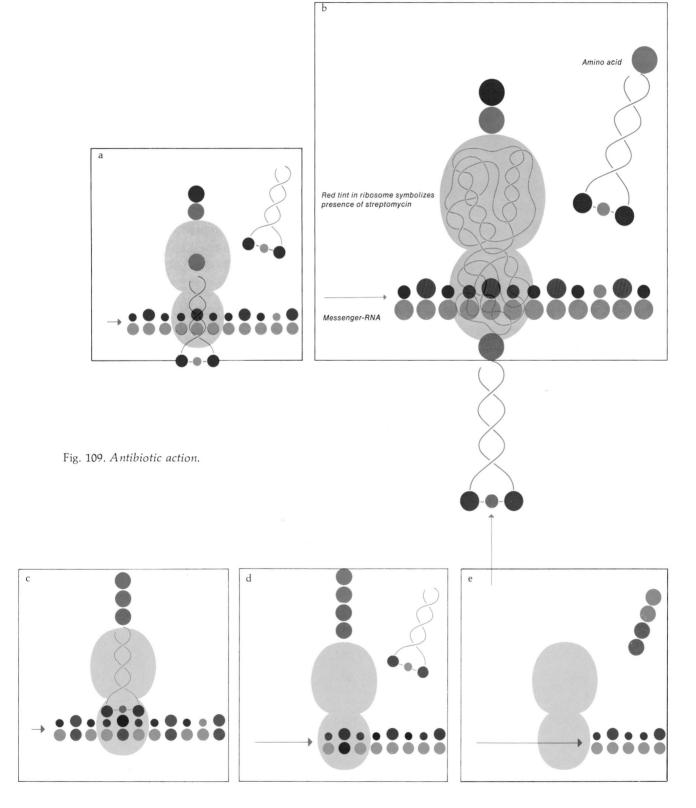

Fig. 109. *Antibiotic action.*

Amino acid

Red tint in ribosome symbolizes
presence of streptomycin

Messenger-RNA

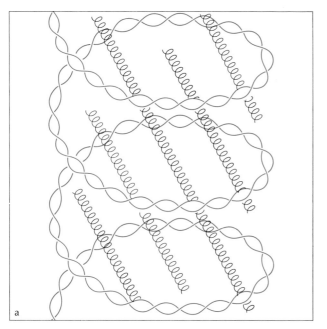

contained a garbled code for an important enzyme, may, in the presence of streptomycin, survive because now the misreadings caused by the drug may at times compensate for the faulty coding and cause a useful enzyme to be made. Such organisms have consequently become streptomycin-dependent and are destroyed when the drug is withdrawn. This phenomenon has frequently been observed in cases of streptomycin resistance.

Discovering the mechanism of action of antibiotics is a complicated problem. Adding a new set of reactions to the list to be investigated complicates the problem further but it also opens up a new area in which to search when satisfactory answers have not been found elsewhere.

Fig. 110. *Repressors and hormone action.*

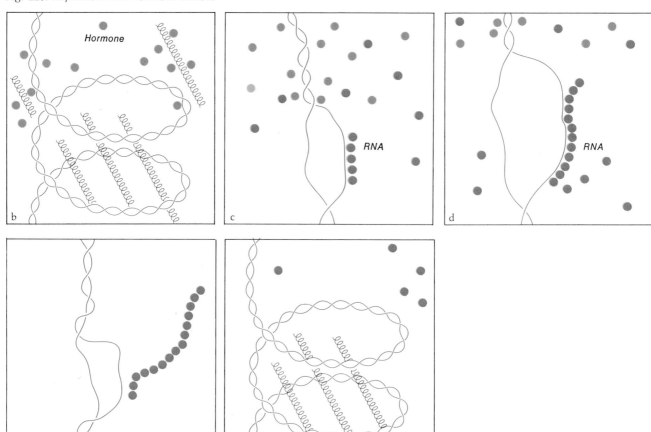

REPRESSORS AND HORMONE ACTION

Up to this point nothing has been said as to how RNA production is controlled. Obviously, some mechanism must exist to start RNA production when it is needed and to stop it when enough has been produced. Consequently, some feedback mechanism must exist. In some cases an excess of a particular sugar inside a cell may stimulate production of the messenger RNA to make the enzyme that will break the sugar down. Reduction of the sugar concentration or the increase in concentration of one of its breakdown products will then stop the RNA production.

Control of RNA production depends on the presence of certain protein molecules on the DNA fibers. These are called repressors and ordinarily prevent separation of the double helix of the DNA and, consequently, of RNA formation. When, however, some substance called an activator combines with the repressor, the repressor's hold on the DNA fiber is loosened and RNA formation can take place. When the activator is removed, for example, by being broken down by the enzyme generated by the RNA, the repressor becomes again attached to the DNA fiber and RNA production ceases.

Such a regulatory mechanism as has just been described is satisfactory when only routine intracellular reactions are involved. When a cell is required to make products not needed for its own metabolic requirements but necessary for proper functioning of the whole community of cells, some other mechanism is required. The production of hemoglobin by the bone marrow cells is such a case. When, because of hemorrhage or other cause, the red blood cell count goes down, a hormone called erythropoietin appears in the blood. This substance stimulates the maturation of bone marrow cells to mature red blood cells. The process can fortunately be studied in tissue culture. E. Goldwasser and associates have shown that when erythropoietin is added to bone marrow cells growing in tissue culture the production of both hemoglobin and stroma protein is stimu-

lated. Furthermore, prior to the increase of these proteins there is an increase in the production of RNA, presumably messenger RNA. This may be brought about by a direct effect of the hormone on the repressors governing the production of the RNA specific for hemoglobin and stroma protein or indirectly. How this may take place is indicated in Figs. 110a-f.

A number of hormones have been shown to bring about increased RNA production as part of their action—in particular, estrogen, androgen and certain of the adrenal hormones. In most instances, because the experiments have to be done on intact animals, the changes brought about by the hormone are so complicated that the exact mechanism of action is very difficult to determine. Differentiation between direct and indirect effects is particularly difficult.

To date, probably the best worked out example of hormonal stimulation of gene activity is the work of Ulrich Clever using ecdysone, the hormone that brings about the molting of the insect larva to produce the pupa. In one such insect, Chironomus tentans, there are two puffs that appear very shortly after the injection of ecdysone —15 minutes to one-half hour. Subsequently, there are a number of other puffs that appear at varying lengths of time after ecdysone injection. All are characterized by the active production of RNA. The appearance of the first two puffs is delayed if actinomycin C, which inhibits RNA production, is given before ecdysone; but puromycin, which inhibits protein synthesis, does not delay their appearance. The latter antibiotic does, however, delay the appearance of all the other puffs. Apparently, therefore, ecdysone somehow directly stimulates the production of two varieties of RNA, but the later puffs are the result directly or indirectly of protein produced by the RNAs from the first two puffs.

Much progress has been made and there is promise that much new information on the DNA-RNA-Protein synthesis system will soon be forthcoming.

Conclusion

Reading this manuscript for the last time before committing it to print I was again conscious of an inherent fault in books like this. The ceaseless restlessness of cells and their ultimate evanescence is inadequately portrayed. I have been able to give only stroboscopic glimpses of structures as they were at the moment of death using only two of their dimensions and sometimes suggesting a third. Of those matters concerned with the fourth dimension, time, such as motion, development and decay, there is only talk. This fault is inherent in all books and can only be remedied by the reader himself observing and experimenting with living creatures in field, clinic and laboratory. Finally, as predicted at the beginning of the book, this treatise cannot hope to be complete and with each passing month will become less and less so. This also is an inherent fault. Poets may perhaps hope that their words will be immortal but any biologist who fosters such a notion should make haste to assess the patency of his cerebral arteries. If, for a time, this book helps give the reader a basic understanding of the subject sufficient for him to appreciate current developments and follow the future ones that pertain to his needs and interests, both the author and publisher will be happy and will be encouraged to start collecting material for the next revision.

Brief Bibliography Including Papers From Which Illustrations Have Been Used

William Bloom and Don W. Fawcett—A Textbook of Histology (1968), W. B. Saunders Company

J. Brachet and A. E. Mirsky—The Cell (6 vol.) 1959-1963, Academic Press, Inc., New York, NY

E. J. DuPraw—Cell & Molecular Biology, Academic Press Inc., New York, NY

Don W. Fawcett—The Cell, an Atlas of Fine Structure (1966), Saunders, Philadelphia, PA

A. W. Ham—Histology (1965), Lippincott, Philadelphia, PA

M. C. Ledbetter and K. R. Porter—An Atlas of Plant Structure (1970), Springer Company, New York, NY

Alex B. Novikoff and Eric Holtzman—Cells and Organelles, Holt, Rinehart and Winston, Inc., New York, NY

A. Loewy and P. Siekevitz—Cell Structure & Function, Holt, New York, 1962

D. F. Kennedy—The Living Cell (1965)—(a collection of articles which appeared in the Scientific American), Freeman, San Francisco, CA

Cold Spring Harbor Symposium of Quantitative Biology, 28, 1963. Synthesis & Structure of Macromolecules

K. R. Porter and M. A. Bonneville—Fine Structure of Cells and Tissues (1965), Lea and Febiger

C. P. Swanson, T. Mertz and W. J. Young—Cytogenetics, Prentice-Hall, Englewood Cliffs, NJ

Thomas E. Everhart and Thomas L. Hayes—The Scanning Electron Microscope, Scientific American, Vol. 226, No. 1, p. 54, Jan., 1972

D. Branton and R. B. Park—Papers on Biological Membrane Structure (1968), Little, Brown and Company, Boston, MA

N. Sharon—The Bacterial Cell Wall, Scientific American, Vol. 220, No. 5, p. 92

V. P. Whittaker—Structure and Function on Animal Cell Membranes, British Medical Bulletin, Vol. 24, No. 2, p. 101, May, 1968

S. J. Singer and L. Nicholson Garth—Fluid Mosaic Model of the Structure of Cell Membranes, Science, Vol. 175, p. 720, Feb., 1972

Fred C. Fox—The Structure of Cell Membranes, Scientific American, Vol. 226, No. 2, p. 30, Feb., 1972

Daniel A. Goodenough and Jean Paul Revel—A Fine Structural Analysis of Intercellular Junctions in Mouse Liver, Journal of Cell Biology, Vol. 45, No. 2, May, 1970

William O. Dobbins III and Emory L. Rollins—Intestinal Mucosal Lymphatic Permeability: An Electron Microscopic Study of Endothelial Vessicles and Cell Junctions, Journal of Ultrastructural Research, Vol. 33, p. 29, Oct., 1970

Werner R. Loewenstein—Intercellular Communication, Scientific American, Vol. 222, No. 5, p. 78, May, 1970

Eric Denton—Reflectors in Fishes, Scientific American, Vol. 224, No. 1, p. 64, Jan., 1971

William J. Larsen—Genesis of Mitochondria in Insect Fat Body, Journal of Cell Biology, Vol. 47, No. 2, Part I, p. 373

John H. Luft—Department of Biological Structure, University of Washington, School of Medicine, Seattle, Washington.

R. Sager—Genes Outside the Chromosome, Scientific American, Vol. 212, No. 1, p. 70, Jan., 1965

Ursula W. Goodenough and R. P. Levine—The Genetic Activity of Mitochondria and Chloroplasts, Scientific American, Vol. 223, No. 5, p. 22, Nov., 1970

Lynn Margolis—Symbiosis and Evolution, Scientific American, Vol. 225, No. 2, p. 48, Aug., 1971

E. Racker—The Membrane of the Mitochondrion, Scientific American, Vol. 218, No. 2, p. 32, Feb., 1968

Keith R. Porter and George E. Palade—Studies on the Endoplasmic Reticulum III, Its Form and Distribution in Striated Muscle, Journal of Cell Biology, Vol. 3, No. 2, p. 269, Mar., 1957

K. R. Porter and C. Franzini—Armstrong—The Sarcoplasmic Reticulum, Scientific American, Vol. 212, No. 3, p. 72

M. Neutra and C. P. Leblond—The Golgi Apparatus, Scientific American, Vol. 220, No. 2, p. 100, Feb., 1969

Daniel S. Friend and Gail E. Brassil—Osmium Staining of Endoplasmic Reticulum and Mitochondria in the Adrenal Cortex, Journal of Cell Biology, Vol. 46, p. 252, 1970

G. Bennett and C. P. Leblond—Formation of Cell Coat Material for the Whole Surface of Columnar Cells in the Rat Small Intestine, as Visualized by Radioautography with L Fucose 3H, Journal of Cell Biology, Vol. 46, p. 409, 1970

John W. Combs—An Electron Microscope Study of Mouse Mast Cells Arising in Vivo and in Vitro, Journal of Cell Biology, Vol. 48, p. 676, 1971

Malcolm R. Brown, Jr., Werner W. Franke, Hans Kleinig, Hans Falk and Pete Sitte—Scale formation in chrysophycean algae. I. Cellulosic & noncellulosic wall components made by the Golgi apparatus, Journal of Cell Biology, Vol. 45, No. 3, p. 246, June, 1970

Charles E. McCall, Isao Katayama, Ramsi S. Cotran and Maxwell Finland—Lysosomal and Ultrastructural Changes in Human Toxic Neutrophils During Bacterial Infection, The Journal of Experimental Medicine, Vol. 129, No. 2, p. 267, Feb., 1969

Walter Fleming—Contributions to the Knowledge of the Cell and its Vital Processes, Part II, A translation and reprinting of one of the classic descriptions of mitosis (1880), Journal of Cell Biology, Vol. 25, No. 1, Part 2, p. 2, Apr., 1965

A. Gibor—Acetabularia: A Useful Giant Cell, Scientific American, Vol. 215, No. 5, p. 118, Nov., 1966

J. B. Gardon—Transplanted Cell Nuclei and Cell Differation, Scientific American, Vol. 219, No. 6, p. 24, Dec., 1968

Theodore Friedmann—Prenatal Diagnosis of Genetic Disease, Scientific American, Vol. 225, No. 5, p. 34, Nov., 1971

Wayne H. Finley, Ph.D., M.D. and Sara Finley, M.D.—Genetic Disorders (pp. 197-218), The Adolescent Patient, C. V. Mosby Company, 1970

Maximo E. Drets and Margery W. Shaw—Specific Banding Patterns in Human Chromosomes, Proc. Natl. Acad. Sci., USA, Vol. 68, No. 9, p. 2073, Sept., 1971

E. J. DuPraw and G. F. Bahr—The Arrangement of DNA in Human Chromosomes, As Investigated by Quantitative Electron Microscopy, Acta Cytologica, Vol. 13, No. 4, p. 188

H. M. Golomb and G. F. Bahr—Scanning Electron Microscopic Observations of Surface Structure of Isolated Human Chromosomes, Science Marchiz, 1971, Vol. 171, p. 1024

J. D. Watson—The Molecular Biology of the Gene (1965), W. A. Benjamin, New York, NY

Hewson Swift—Nucleic Acids and Cell Morphology in Dipteran Salivary Glands, "Molecular Control of Cellular Activity," J. Allen (ed.), McGraw Hill, 1962

H. Ris—B. Chromosomes and Genes, Fine Structure of Chromosomes, Proceedings of the Royal Society, B, Vol. 164, p. 246, 1966

Joseph G. Gall—Chromosomes & Cytodifferentiation, Cytodifferential & Macromolecular Synthesis, 1963, Academic Press, Inc.

Hans Ris and Barbara L. Chandler—Ultrastructure of Genetic Systems in Prokaryotes & Eukaryotes, Cold Spring Harbor Symposia on Quantitative Biology, Vol. XXVIII, 1963

S. S. Spiegelman—Hybrid Nucleic Acids, Scientific American, May, 1964, p. 48

Wolfgang Beermann and Ulrich Clever—Chromosome Puffs, Scientific American, Vol. 210, No. 4, p. 49, Apr., 1964

Oscar L. Miller, Jr. and Barbara R. Beatty—Portrait of a Gene, Journal of Cellular Physiology, Supplement I to Vol. 74, No. 2, Part 2, p. 225

O. L. Miller, Jr., Barbara R. Beatty, Barbara A. Hamkalo and C. A. Thomas, Jr.—Electron Microscope Visualization of Transcription, Cold Spring Harbor, Symposium of Quantitative Biology

Russell Ross and Earl P. Benditt—Wound Healing and Collagen Formation, The Journal of Cell Biology, Vol. 22, p. 365, 1964

R. Ross—Wound Healing, Scientific American, Vol. 220, No. 6, p. 40

M. Nomara—Ribosomes, Scientific American, Vol. 221, No. 4, p. 28, Oct., 1969

J. Davis, W. Gilbert and L. Gorini—Streptomycin Suppression of the Code, Proc. Natl. Academy of Science, Vol. 51, p. 883, 1964

Odette Gallien-Lartigue and Eugene Goldwasser—On the Mechanism of Erythropoietin-Induced Differentiation, Biochimic et Biophysica Acta, Vol. 103, p. 219 (1965)

Mark Ptashne and Walter Gilbert—Genetic Repressors, Scientific American, Vol. 222, No. 6, p. 36, June, 1970